Melvin Van Peebles,
a remarkably versatile and talented artist, has been
critically acclaimed for his jazz compositions and film-
making.

A BEAR FOR THE FBI

is Van Peebles' fifth book. It is the deceptively simple
story—direct and candid—of a black suburban child
making it to manhood. The novel opens with a boy's first
memories; it closes with his college graduation. The route
is familiar, but the treatment is not—for in the ordinary
resides the extraordinary, and Van Peebles has mined it.

In the sounds and silences, defeats and victories of
middle-class family life is revealed "the depth of the
human heart and what a dreamer it is and how lonely
it can be."

A Bear for the FBI

was originally published by Trident Press.

MELVIN VAN PEEBLES

A BEAR
FOR THE
FBI

PUBLISHED BY POCKET BOOKS NEW YORK

A BEAR FOR THE FBI

Trident Press edition published September, 1968

A *Pocket Book* edition

1st printing .... September, 1969

This *Pocket Book* edition includes every word
contained in the original, higher-priced edition. It is printed
from brand-new plates made from completely reset, clear, easy-to-read
type. *Pocket Book* editions are published by Pocket Books, a division
of Simon & Schuster, Inc., 630 Fifth Avenue, New York, N.Y. 10020.
Trademarks registered in the United States and other countries.

Standard Book Number: 671—75455—6.
Library of Congress Catalog Card Number: 68—26709.
Copyright, ©, 1968, by Melvin Van Peebles. All rights reserved.

Printed in the U.S.A.

*This book is dedicated to just about
everybody except the sonofabitches who were
always telling me "You can't."*

A writer sent an article to a well-known magazine. The magazine replied, we like your article, however, we think your title, *A Bear*, is a little bland, can you give us something more provocative.

The writer thought and thought and finally came up with the title, *I Screwed a Bear*. The magazine replied, good, but your field of appeal is limited, see if you can't work in something with more general interest in it. Suggestion: undercover stories are very popular at present.

The writer came up with the title, *I Screwed a Bear for the FBI,* and he sent it in. Fine, the magazine replied, very close, but the overall effect is a little paganistic, a little sacrilegious don't you agree.

At last the writer came up with a satisfactory title, *I Screwed a Bear for the FBI and Found God*. Excellent, the magazine replied, and printed the story under the heading, THE MOST MEMORABLE ANIMAL I EVER MET.

1

Jesus Christ, man, I don't know—I suppose I have no right to say anything—I read about the air battle of England, or I hear of the men inch by inch that scraped their guts out crawling over the coral of the Pacific at Tarawa and Bougainville fighting the Japs, or I read *The Autobiography of Lincoln Steffens,* or I remember Kafka's syntax, or the precociousness of Raymond Radiguet, I don't even have a neat package marked CONCLUSIONS; all I did was come up in Chicago on the South Side until I was in the fifth grade and we moved to the suburbs. I never got to live off earthworms, or saw people screwing in the open daylight because they were going to die in a gas chamber in a few hours. I finished grade school and went to Webster High, a wonderful place if you were normal, or acceptable abnormal, but a Dachau, or Corregidor if you weren't. Europeans say sagely, a little tolerantly, a little overbearingly, "You Americans . . . you don't know what suffering, or hardship means." (They shake their heads wisely, the way adults who feel they have the inside track on the sadness of responsibility do when they hear a child say he wishes he were grown.) I want to say I didn't make the track team and that I missed the senior prom, but what is a prom to being bombed, or a life—nothing I guess, yet at the time I would gladly have traded my arms for an evening of dancing and being big and being the first one through the tape. Maybe each heart is given the same amount of emotions for a lifetime regardless of the circumstances; so much hate and pity, love and fear per person, issued methodically the way some girls pass out their kisses: one kiss the first date, two kisses the second, and two kisses and a couple of pats the third, etc., and if the heart doesn't have bullets, or third movements, or escapes, to worry about it settles for hair dyes and football pools. Maybe a lonely old man whose cat is run over is as sad and grief-stricken as a mother whose only son drowns on a summer afternoon. In eighth grade the war ended and we were left stranded without even a paper drive to give us a morning off. In high school everyone wore fatigues their big brothers had brought back from the service. If you didn't have a big brother you bought a couple of used pairs from a surplus store. I don't know—a fellow who lived down the street from me was a pilot, he was just a rummy when I got to know him, but once he spent two weeks on a life raft in the ocean. Man, I can't help it if I never got shot at, or anything. My folks weren't even poor. The only spot of color, the only banner in the whole goddamn thing was that we were Negroes.

We weren't far enough South, being young and uniniti-
ated, though for this to seem to be an insurmountable
disadvantage. When I was young I used to get my kicks
in race dreams. I daydreamed that I was going to be a
colored Mahatma Gandhi, or sometimes I would lie
on the living room floor and read about lynch mob vio-
lence. I always pictured myself breaking up a ferocious
mob and rescuing a poor servant girl who it later turned
out wasn't a real maid, but an African princess, or if
the victim I saved was a boy we would hide in a shack,
or under a bridge and his beautiful sister would risk her
life to bring us food, her dress would be all wet with
perspiration and it would cling to her skin showing
everything she had. After a while I hated any injustice
I could make out which can get pretty complicated,
also after a while the sharpness of being a Negro, the
paradox of the thing, wears off and you get used to it
just as if you have a wooden leg, or one eye and you
don't notice it unless you come to a high curb, or apply
for a job where the color line hasn't been broken. We
are raised to be pioneers, killers of Indians, finders of
oil, conquerors of bad nations, but there were no fron-
tiers and my mother would have smashed my head if I
had smoked and I was way too young to drink, so I
turned to God for intensity and went through that phase
for a time. Maybe this is an age of change, and action,
and revolution, and upheaval of traditions and nations
as I once heard a speaker say. I was sitting in a college
assembly at the time and as the speaker talked I felt
myself caught up in his words. I visualized the panora-
ma of history, people swept by surging on toward a
goal like Hollywood extras in a big technicolor mob
scene; later it occurred to me that you can't spend your
life surging along as irresistible forces of humanity, you

must stop to eat and sleep and go to the toilet and someone has to be preparing the food and mending the clothes for the tide when it gets tired. We can't even all be extras, or exceptional. So maybe I shouldn't say anything. Perhaps a war will come along, or a decisive moment and when we die at least our bodies can be monuments to democracy, or science, or upheavals of tradition, or something.

2

When i was born a stork flew over the zoo fence circled three times and began to climb into the sky. He flew higher and higher; finally he reached the fleecy clouds that cover the earth, still he climbed. At last, up ahead, he saw his destination, the angel. The stork flew up to the angel and the angel hooked a diaper, with me in it, over the stork's bill. Then the stork started his return journey back to earth. After a long time he reached the hospital where my Mother was waiting and he flew through the window and left me upon her bed. This is how I was born, or at least this is the version my Mother gave me and when I was little I believed I remembered the whole proceeding. If I concentrated real hard I could even remember how the wind felt whistling past my ears when I was being carried in the diaper and the peculiar odor of stork feathers. At night I often prayed to the Lord to turn me into a stork so I could see an angel—later when I found out I couldn't possibly have experienced what I was more than emphatically positive I did remember, I began to doubt Absoluteness.

Before I went to school, when I was very small, I wanted to be a minister. Maybe I only thought I wanted to be a minister, which, as far as I can see, is quite the same thing; perhaps my selection was due to environment, or destiny, or to a firemanlike, tarzanlike romantic appeal that being a preacher implied to me; but notwithstanding my early choice by the time I was twelve I had switched ideals and I wanted with all my heart to be a pimp.

I came to on a Sunday morning, i.e., the first thing I can remember, or a number of Sunday mornings. A newsboy passed below yelling extra, extra, dragging out the words, eexxtraa get your Suunday mornning paappeer and my mother putting white shoes on me and saying warm things to me and something about a brown and yellow basket and somebody who could, or couldn't go back to their mommy.

I came to in the front bedroom, the bedroom overlooking the street, in an apartment with a long hall. I guess, the front bedroom was where I heard the newspaper boys chanting below the windows as they went up and down the avenue on Sundays. The hall stretched nearly the length of the apartment. The hall started at my parents' bedroom in the front, where I stayed, and ended at the dining room in the rear, where my Cousin Ethel slept; the dining room in turn opened into Grandmother's room and the kitchen. It's funny why I remember that hall so well. For me the big unhappiness

14

of that time was when my Mother punished me for some infraction of the rules of proper conduct. She'd spank me a few taps and then disown me, giving me the silent treatment. "Say something to me, Mother," I'd plead, but she wouldn't answer me. I would begin to cry and stamp my feet repeating over and over, "Say something to me, Mother." Finally she would look down at me and say very solemnly, "You don't have a Mother anymore." I would sob with grief, believing every word; then after a while I would go and walk up and down the long gloomy hall, rubbing the wallpaper for security and saying to myself, "Nobody loves me, nobody loves me." Halfway down the hall was another bedroom which belonged to my auntie and uncle. On one side of their bedroom toward the back was the bathroom. On the other side of their bedroom was the living room, but it wasn't really a living room anymore, Auntie had converted it into a studio for her clients. Auntie read minds and it was she who first noticed the divine spark in me and announced to the rest of the family that I was chosen to be a minister.

Sometimes my mother would be overwhelmed with joy, her good fortune seemed unbelievable to her and she would prod my aunt for reassurances, "Carol, do you really think Edward is going to be a minister?" she would ask. Auntie would God's-will her and talk about a vision and lift me up onto the piano bench where I would recite Bible verses I had been taught at Auntie's class.

Everyday Auntie would hold class in her studio for the three of us: my two cousins, Cousin Ralph who was eleven months older than I was, Cousin Ethel who was a big girl going on ten, and me. At class we would study a verse from the Bible and Auntie would tell us a

15

story and just talk about things in general. Auntie explained the universe in terms of love, goodness, the Bible, and her imagination. She was also a little dogmatic in her sweetness. She made us promise not to fight one another, or ever lie; she made us promise to say our prayers, to be good, not to bully, and to always turn the other cheek. Until I started to school that apartment, especially the studio, was my universe and as far as I knew the world was just as Auntie said it was, in fact I have never really recovered from my early training in the goodness of man and as a result I am a gullible sonofabitch.

We went to the studio everyday; however we never grew tired of it and entering the studio, which was normally off-limits to us, was an adventure equal to taking a boat ride in a South Sea war-canoe (now I suspect Auntie slyly forbade us freedom of the studio to increase its value). Once inside we knelt and said a short prayer. Then Auntie would sprinkle us with holy water and say, "Get up, kiddies." We would stand up, our eyes as big as saucers and gaze around the studio which never ceased to enthrall us, there were a million things to bewitch; there were Bibles and religious tracts scattered over the room, there were figurines of Jesus and Mary and saints, there was a Buddha with a place for incense between his legs which he held in a funny position, there were two bowls of goldfish, crosses of every description with and without Jesus bleeding on them, a rosary, three or four nativity scenes left over from various Christmases, angel hair, an electric heater and dark blue placards with silver writing hanging on the walls. Since I could not read, the placards fascinated me more than anything else in the room. Sometimes Auntie would read a placard and then discuss the slogan with us. The slogans on Auntie's placards all took one of two paths, either "Look World! I'm a Christian," or "Things are tough now, but in the sweet-bye-and-bye I'll get my Heavenly pension." The "Look World" placards weren't hard to understand; for instance the placard, HIS FEET ARE ALWAYS WELCOME AT THIS HEARTH wasn't too hard to understand once Auntie explained what a hearth was and that HIS FEET meant God, but the other path, the "Tough now —pension later" path which implied the horror of living and a sweetness in laying the mortal burden down was beyond our comprehension. Auntie would explain as best she could, but it was useless, it was like trying to explain color to blind people. At the time we were still virgins to troubles and tribulations. The apartment was our whole world and all life was carefully sifted for us and the lumps of unpleasant reality tossed away. Of course, we left the apartment to go to church, or Christmas shopping, or to run in the park, yet its atmosphere was always around us like a gigantic bowl and we saw the world much as Auntie's goldfish did. We were tadpoles. No, we weren't even tadpoles, we were frog eggs. Deep in the pond of the family we lived. The splash caused by the Depression didn't reach us. Even the periodic waves of adult dissension never reached us; like the time, for example, when Auntie refused to send Cousin Ethel to public school saying that the kids there were too bad and tough for Ethel to associate with and that she would teach her herself and Mom replied that Ethel was a little devil and that the kids at school would have to go some to be worse than Ethel and one thing led to another and Auntie and Mother got angry with one another and stopped speaking for three months, except when we were around.

17

Whenever Auntie had a new client she would call us into her studio one by one to introduce us. Sometimes she would call Ralph first and sometimes Ethel, but she always called me last. When I came into the studio the client would gaze at me kindly, bored, tolerantly, a trifle weary of sweet little kids, but hoping by showing interest that Auntie would knock a bit off her mind-reading fee which was pretty steep. Then Auntie would pull me forward and spring it on them.

"This is my nephew, Edward (pat, pat), our little minister." The client would become very interested, gushing congratulations at Auntie and smiling at me. Sometimes Auntie would just introduce me by mentioning my name and saying, "Ed, tell the lady what you're going to be when you grow up."

"A preacher-missionary and I want to go . . ." at this point I would always be interrupted by the clients: Grand, How fine, Lord-be-praised. To which Auntie would: Yes girl, Smart-as-a-whip girl. Auntie would squeeze me to her side, never rising from her chair, and then she would usher me out into the hall again.

That is the way life went for me until I was six, getting up in the mornings, taking two naps then only one nap a day and unvaryingly in bed by seven-thirty or eight. I can only remember once that I was permitted to stay up past eight, that was the time the church had a midnight candlelight service. Auntie said she thought we, my cousins and myself, should be allowed to go. This caused quite a sensation.

Grandmother said no the night air. But Auntie pointed out the night air surely wouldn't hurt us going to do the Lord's work. Mother didn't think we should be up that late, midnight was very late. The service wouldn't last until midnight, it's just called that. That's

18

true. Auntie said furthermore we could sleep until it was almost time to go and stay in bed late the next day. You will never be able to keep them in bed late, Grandmother said. Just once wouldn't hurt them. No, Mother said, she guessed it wouldn't. Grandma still disagreed. Auntie said it would be good for us. Grandma said she never heard of such a thing, dragging children out in the middle of the night. It won't be very late. Yes, but they won't be back until almost midnight. Auntie talked some more and Grandmother walked away muttering about pneumonia and left Mother with Auntie, which was as good as admitting defeat. So it was decided we should go.

When the night of the candlelight service arrived both my cousins were sick with sore throats. Auntie still wanted to take them, but Grandmother said over her dead body. Grandmother told Auntie to go ahead to service and she would stay and nurse the children. Auntie said no she would stay and nurse the children and for Grandmother to go ahead. Grandmother said no. Auntie said no. Neither would be out-martyred and so Mother and I went alone. That night when I would have normally been asleep we left the apartment.

We walked down the stairs and through the vestibule, Mom opened the door and we stepped into the street. When Mom opened the door and we stepped outside I entered a world I had never known, until then I had only known the character of our part of town during the day; but the city is more than one single character, the city is more than one single personality—at different times and places the city is a different person.

During the day in our section the city was a young laborer with glistening arms, confident in the strength of his back, or a stockboy for Montgomery Ward—both

19

paying for a wristwatch and an imitation diamond on time. But when we stepped into the street it was a new world for me. The laborer and stockboy, the day men, were gone, it was the city's intermediate period, the transition between day and night. Now the city was more like a heavyset philosophical domestic who has just come home and taken off her tight downtown shoes. During the intermediate period the streets are quiet. Early whiskyheads making the rounds find the bars almost empty and they choose favorite hangouts and retire quietly to corners to wait for things to happen, awed by the empty silence; they sip their drinks and maybe contemplate Why and make resolutions; they talk to the bartenders, or watch the puddles their glasses leave—just marking time, waiting for the intermediate period to end, waiting for things to fill up and live. In summer the intermediate period is the time when the dinners of salmon croquettes and cabbage have been eaten and people are sitting on the back porches of the tenements; the men sit with their shirts unbuttoned, or without shirts and the radio which has been moved from the living room to the kitchen where it can be heard better from the outside is turned up completely, going full blast, serenading the folks as they talk. The L that roars by is only half full, not almost empty, three or four persons scattered in a coach as it will be later unless something is going on downtown, or packed as it was three quarters of an hour before, but half full. On the streets of the city everything is so becalmed and unfamiliar you might think you are lost in a strange land. In the rural districts the intermediate period is the time when a farmer going out to the barn to take a last look around hears a train whistle in the distance and wonders where people are going and how would it be to be sitting in a coach hurtling somewhere into the darkness. In the country the intermediate period may last for an hour, or an hour and a half, but in the city it is much shorter and lasts only twenty or thirty minutes, and then Mr. Night takes over. At night the city is the laborer, or stockboy again, but grown older. Mr. Night is chubbier; his aspirations have been decayed by time; he has two children, his apartment smells of pies and he wears a new overly expensive shirt. Something about Mr. Night reminds you of a young girl that has been caught and raped beneath the L's superstructure— at least that was the city in my section.

My mother was a fast walker and we arrived at the church before the intermediate period ended. I had never seen the church after dark before; its peaks and spirals loomed up majestically against the dark sky. Inside, the church was not packed as it was on Sundays. It was only a third full with most of the people gathered down front near the pulpit.

There were no other children there and I began to strut as we went down the aisle to take seats. People asked Mother about me. My isn't that a sweet little boy. How old is he? He doesn't seem the least bit sleepy. Only four? Mother explained that I was going to be a minister when I grew up and that I wanted to come so badly. My future was batted around and praised. How the Lord needed fresh new blood to carry on his work. You can never start too young.

Exactly on time the minister began the service. He was happy to see so many of us coming to the House of the Lord to worship. I was sure the minister was looking directly at me and I swelled with pride.

After the invocation everyone stood up and filed past the pulpit where an usher handed each person a lighted

21

candle; everyone that is except Mrs. King and me. Mrs. King was too weak and Mother said I was too small to go marching around in the dark and that I was to sit still like a good boy.

Mrs. King was the oldest member of the church. She was a very rickety, feeble old lady with a scraggly beard and unless she was bedridden she never missed a service. She was so old she couldn't hold her water anymore. Sometimes she would have to go and when she did she would just scoot forward in her seat and wet. The floor was slanted downward toward the pulpit and after a while a big damp spot would appear on the new carpet in front of the preacher's rostrum. Sometimes halfway through the Sunday service she would fall asleep. When she didn't fall asleep she'd mutter amens out loud and if she became filled with the love of God she would begin to sing, even if the minister was in the middle of his sermon. Her pitiful old voice would cut in on the sermon. I couldn't ever recognize the tune, but someone would and they would begin to help her along, then another voice would join in, finally the whole church would take up the song and they would sing verse after verse, and every now and then Mrs. King's squeaky old voice would break through on top off key. The singing always made me feel squirmy, like the last scene of marine war movies made me feel; the part when the band begins to play, quietly at first and then louder and louder, and the camera pans the battlefield and you hear rifle shots, da da ping da, and two marines who have been fighting each other throughout the movie suddenly understand one another and a flicker of camaraderie passes between them and the tempo of the music quickens and the heroes start running forward and the troops move in on the enemy.

Suddenly the lights were all turned off. I wasn't frightened at first. All I could see were the little flickering dots that were the lights from the candles. The candles formed a line and began to march around and around the church singing. It's hard to explain, but I don't think I really had to be frightened, but they kept going around and around so I became bored and I began to prod myself with fear for entertainment, opening the floodgate of my imagination. Suppose my mother has left me—I felt a thrill of fear . . . when the dew is still on the roses, they sang. When the lights went off Mrs. King was sitting in a pew two rows behind me, suddenly I knew she was coming to eat me. The line moved slowly around the church singing. I bet she's right behind me . . . wade in the water, wade in the water, they sang. Suppose God has called them to heaven . . . maybe they aren't people. Mommy, Mommy, I thought. He walks with me and talks with me, they sang . . . I thought of a picture in Auntie's studio painted on black velvet, it was a picture of Jesus praying with his hands folded and resting on a big rock. Coming for to carry me, they sang. I knew the old lady was behind me. She was ready to pounce on me her face was all squinched up just the way Cousin Ethel imitated her, her fingernails were long and green. Mrs. King leaped out of the dusk at me her face luminous and her mouth bleeding. I shall not be, I shall not be— I screamed. Nothing happened. I screamed again. The lights came on—everyone was there. I whirled around. The old lady was asleep two rows behind me, or pretending to be. My mother came over and told me that was no way for a future preacher to act, but I wouldn't stop crying and since the service was nearly over we left.

Outside it was quiet, but it wasn't the young, family, peaceful silence of the intermediate period; Mr. Night had arrived in full force, it was a different quiet, it was a deceitful, hoping to forget, hoping to postpone, carefree, first ditch and last ditch quiet. It was seven blocks from the church to our apartment: a half block up to 55th Boulevard, three blocks over to South Park Avenue, and then three and a half blocks down South Park to home.

On 55th Boulevard a half block before South Park there was a nightclub. It sat flush with the sidewalk between a place that was later turned into a bowling alley, I don't remember what it was at the time, and a filling station. As we neared the nightclub the music got louder and louder, it seemed to come to a crescendo, people were clapping and yelling and shouting. I had never seen a bar at night before when it was really rolling. Just as we came abreast of the nightclub a man came out. When he opened the door the noise jumped out and washed over us. The man also bumped into us, but Mom swerved out of his path. He tried to focus his eyes. "Excuse me, lady," he said, and then he went down the street the way he had just come from. I stood fascinated by the happiness coming from behind the bar door. "Come, Ed," my mother said and when she saw my interest in the bar she explained things to me. She told me how the music and laughter was lowdown nigger music and laughter and told me I was big enough to start to understand things and explained to me about sin, the sin of drinking and swearing and loud music and she talked vaguely about bad women and men without ever defining her terms. We were at the corner and so we turned and started down South Park which was all apartment buildings, no neon signs and you could

24

see the sky dark blue overhead. When Mom finished explaining things to me I thought she would mention church and how I had cried, but she never did. Finally we reached our apartment building. Before we went upstairs Mom made me promise to sleep late so that Grandmother wouldn't be mad and I promised her I would.

3

THE TRAMP OF THE SS TROOPERS' BOOTS in the dark street of an occupied country never stoked more terror in a heart than the patter of my classmates' little feet as we went to the schoolyard for recess and more than likely I was due for another ass-kicking, nor was a person more conspicuous, even a Jew with his mandatory star, than I was in my busterbrown collar, short pants and knobby knees that my mother thought was so cute among my long pants classmates. Finally we would be outside in the gravel-laid playground; once there recess would fall into the unvarying pattern for me of fight-and-lose. I was the worst fighter in the second grade, which of course made me a very popular opponent; in the morning before recess some action of mine would be mutilated and misconstrued into a challenge for a fight. The school was crowded and we went in half-day shifts, even then sitting two to a desk—stupid, uncomfortable, there were plenty of chances for trouble: a dropped pencil, an answered question, or someone thinking you looked like you thought you were tough, then I would get an ominous wink, or a nudge when we were marched to the toilet. That would be it, I would get it again.

"Why'd you push my pencil?" we would be in the schoolyard now.

"I didn't," I would say as unoffensively as possible. When forced into a fight my tactics consisted in putting up only a token resistance, hoping to be let off easy and holding back the tears.

"You did, Stupid."

"When?" I asked. Stall, stall. As soon as the teachers finished grabbing quick smokes they would be out to monitor us.

"You know . . ." and it would start.

"Quit."

"Don't push me."

"You pushed me."

"Well, don't. YOU, push Me, . . . Knees." Gradually we would drift away from the school to the perimeter of the playground which ended suddenly at the sidewalk. There the ring of children would be encompassed, circled and recircled with kibitzing adults who happened to pass. Some men stood quietly, others shouted advice just as if they had money on us.

"Hold your guard up there . . . short pants."

"That's it, big boy . . . no, one-two, one-two."

"Mix it up," they would discuss our merits and potentials heatedly, putting their heads together and ges-

28

turing with mangled cigarettes. The women clucked their tongues and shook their heads in disgust.

"Ruffians . . ."

"It takes two to make a fight."

"I wish one of them was mine. I'd fan his bottommm gooood."

When two men got into a fight someone called the police, but our little hands looked so puny and by comparison the whacks we traded were lovepats no one even bothered to stop us, except a teacher. However the blows were landing on small eyes and noses, to me they seemed lethal and I was in mortal fear of getting killed, but in second grade I had to wait for a teacher to stop us, one would finally amble over and break it up, pick me up, wipe me off and pull the pebbles from my knees. The winner would stand there with his lower lip pushed out and his fists doubled heaving his chest exaggeratedly telling me, "I'm not through, Sonofabitch." I didn't even listen—recess was over, maybe he would forget about it tomorrow, if he did there would be someone else, but recess was over—I didn't think about it. I was safe. Mother took me to school and carried me home every day—I was the only boy in the whole class whose mother did that. Not even the cripple boy's mother did that—I planned to jump on the cripple boy and beat him up as soon as I got a little stronger, he was a pretty muscular boy with massive arms and a gimpy leg, now I realize he was only fat, but then it was massive muscle and I was afraid of him.

I went to school in the morning shifts and toward noon which was the end of my school day I would get so frightened I would begin to whimper to myself and squirm in my seat, my waist felt as if I needed a belt —suppose my mother was not waiting for me.

Going through the hall the guy I fought with at recess would sidle up to me in line hardly waiting until we got outside to resume hostilities. We would march outside and he would raise a fist, there would be my mother and the guy would draw back frightened and hurry away the picture of decorum. My mother would be standing on the sidewalk smiling and waiting for me. I would hate her. When I got near her I would make sounds to show my disgust of her as loud as I dared, so everyone could see I wanted no part of her help. Maybe Mom knew how scared I was and how glad I was to see her, or, which is more likely, she just wasn't trusting precious to make it the three blocks home in one piece patrol boys, or no patrol boys and there she was waiting with the same smile she brought me to school with— Now, Edward, I know you think you're a man, but you're still a little boy yet. Only twice during the year I was in second grade did she miss picking me up on time, that is what I am telling about, not the first time when all that happened is I got my ass kicked on the run for three blocks, but the second time.

A number of weeks before my mother was late for the second time I had started to take boxing lessons from my Cousin Jo-Jo. The lessons began insignificantly enough with Jo-Jo, who was a delivery boy for my Dad after school and on weekends, being bored. There wasn't much work during the week and he hit upon the idea of teaching me boxing to pass the time. Cousin Jo-Jo was not a real boxer, but since he was seventeen I trusted him unconditionally with the naïve assurance that small boys have, believing that men are proficient and familiar with everything; his instructions were as venerated as if they had come from the mighty Joe Louis himself; nor did the fact that my cousin con-

30

stantly referred to a boxing magazine that he had found abandoned in the pocket of a jacket to be cleaned undermine my Gibraltar faith. We talked shop: uppercuts, shadow boxing, footwork—sometimes he read me his favorite story from the boxing magazine—the biography of a trainer and how he made champions—I was to be Jo-Jo's champion. We even designed a training schedule, which my mother vetoed, but I gave up eating black pepper, which I liked, to show I was in the proper spirit. But as far as connecting the two—the battles in the schoolyard and my lessons in the manly art— I did not believe in myself enough so it never occurred to me. I went on day after day getting my ass kicked at recess. Yet the beatings weren't completely losses, blow by blow I gained my first two subtitles, Roman numerals I and II in my mental outline, entitled PHILOSOPHY OF LIFE. First subtitle: ducking can often be as effective as swinging. Some people don't mind how much of a beating they take as long as they get a chance to give a few lumps; but not me, I don't see landing two blows even if I only get one in return. (These may seem like awfully long subtitles for an outline, but it is only when you try to put them into words that they become cumbersome, in my mind they are condensed to symbols, similar to π in mathematics.) The second subtitle concerns bullies. If a fellow bullies you and he can't be avoided ask him to stop; then ask him once more, but if he doesn't stop after you ask him twice, fight him—eventually the situation will become intolerable and no matter how frightened you are you will have to fight him and in the meantime you will have taken all that extra bullying. If a bully doesn't stop after he has been asked twice he is not going to stop at all unless he is more actively discouraged. He isn't going to have a

31

sudden change of heart at the seventh, or eighth request, yet many people go through life in this manner hoping for a change of heart, hoping by some sudden reversal to be delivered from their tormentors. They expect an unlikely miracle to save them. I say unlikely not because the size of the miracle required is too large, but from the opposite reason. Most of the bullying we endure is commonplace, even humdrum; however miracles, acts of clemency and changes of heart are usually whooping gestures made in big sweeping areas: the blind seeing, the lame walking, John Smith, amnesty for all prisoners, etc. Who ever heard of a humdrum miracle? But people go along taking crap and hoping for a reprieve when they should go whack the bully—of course, now don't get me wrong, they may not win, but bullies are notorious cowards and there are so many, many waiter-and-hopers to pick on that if a person stands up for his rights chances are he can get away with it.

Even if Jo-Jo had really known how to train me my lessons were of little value without actual experience in offensive fighting, which I didn't have and which my classmates had in abundance—long before I went to school, when my Mother was holding me on her lap and telling me fairy tales: *The Queen in the Tower, Hansel and Gretel, The Good Blind Prince,* or traveling half-way across the city to find a suitable play-partner for me, my future classmates were learning to protect themselves in the Darwinlike jungle of slum childhood. By the time they reached school age they were veteran fighters, long since past the windmilling stage. They did not fight one another with little yelps and a few babyish swipes, but with doubled fists and once the fight actually began there was little talking, they circled around each other cautiously avoiding the edge of the circle, their eyes full of hate and determination. On the ground they scuffled and wrestled, their feet milling in the air, the next moment scrambling in the dirt for leverage for the flip unto the top, or for stability to stay on top, all the time only grunting and panting with exertion. This little man seriousness always fascinated the grownups crowded around watching—I had no experience and I should have known better, but Cousin Jo-Jo's lessons gave me confidence and my confidence grew so large until one day, the second time my Mother was late, my mind lost its protective-caution and tied the two facts together, the fights I had to face and the boxing lessons Jo-Jo gave me to amuse himself; that is when I decided that my persecution had gone far enough and I was going to teach Baby Brother, who happened to be the third toughest kid in class, a lesson as far as fighting went.

That morning the teacher had given us colored paper and crayons to draw. Knowing that orange was my favorite color she gave the only sheet to me; unfortunately Baby Brother, who had a nose like a double barreled shotgun and who was a real rough customer, decided he wanted it.

"Give it here," he whispered.

"No, Baby Brother."

"If you know what's good for you . . . you'll give it here."

"I'll call the teacher."

"I'll see you at recess, Knees."

I shook my head.

"I'll see you at recess . . . Big Head." (I didn't have a big head. Accuracy wasn't important, Baby Brother was just calling me names to show his power.)

The teacher walked among us while we drew mur-

muring encouragement over our masterpieces. The preparatory recess bell rang and we lined up to go to the playground—for all the fear I felt it could have been to the gas chamber; as I grew older I learned to ration my fear: I was so frightened of a bad report card, not quite as frightened when I was late from school, terribly frightened of being castrated—each terror had a specific amount of fear, but that day I was frightened as only a child can be—a child without a precept, or rationalization to fall back on—I would get it again. The teacher looked up from her desk where she was going through our drawings and saved me. "Ed," she said, "please come here."

I got out of line.

"Is this yours?" she asked holding up my drawing.

The second bell rang and the class marched out without me.

"Yes, Mam."

"I think it shows promise."

"Yes, Mam."

"Well, is that all you have to say? If that is all you have to say . . ."

"Yes, Mam, I mean No, Mam . . . I like to draw I do a lot, I really like to draw, I could draw all day . . . at home I've got a picture I drew all by myself . . . I gave it to my Mother."

"Well, that's nice, Ed. You keep practicing, some day you may be a Gainsborough, or Reynolds, of course you don't know them, but they were great painters."

"Yes, Mam."

She looked at the clock on the wall. "Well, recess is almost half over. I know you want to go out and play with the other children."

"Yes, Mam." I did not move.

"Go on shoo . . . go get your exercise. . . . Well, go on."

I sidled out of the room as slow as I could. The hall was empty. I ducked into the toilet and stayed there, sitting on one of the bowls, until recess was over, in that way I planned to escape the wrath of Baby Brother and I would have if my Mother had been there waiting for me after school, to hate and clutch and to go home with.

Suddenly it was almost noon and I sat at my desk with the last minute blues. You are supposed to adjust to anything, nevertheless, everyday when school was almost out I got that frightened feeling. I wanted to cry too, but I had learned the folly of tears. Tears were to my classmates what blood is to a school of sharks. If you cried they doubled their persecution. The preliminary bell rang and we lined up, two abreast and there was Baby Brother one row behind me, grinning with his gap teeth and shotgun nose. The dismissal bell rang and we marched out.

We burst out into the sunshine—Baby Brother one row behind—there was Mother. I was safe. I started toward the spot where she always stood out of habit. Then I realized I hadn't seen her. She hadn't come. Baby Brother was coming toward me, "Hi, Mom," I yelled and waved at the sidewalk as if my mother were there. Baby Brother ducked his head down and shuffled past me. I started hurrying toward home. I was at the sidewalk—he hadn't caught on. . . . I was at the street, the patrol boy held us for a car then he let us through, Baby Brother hadn't caught on, the stupid old dumb thing. . . . I beat everyone across the street. I began to skip so it wouldn't look like I was running—I saw Knees running home yesterday. Of course I was smart,

I had fooled that dumb old Baby Brother, he never even looked up—I beat that dumb old thing, he thought Mom was there. I was at the alley, then the next corner. I dashed across the street. Boy was he dumb. I fooled him, humph, he thought Mom had come for me like she always did, ha, ha. . . . I don't need her—I was at the middle of the second block.

"Where's your murther, Knees?" Baby Brother stepped out of the alley. "Why didn't you give me the paper, Knees . . . think you're smart doncha?"

"Fight," someone yelled and we were instantly surrounded.

"What is it?"

"Baby Brother is gonna kick Knees's ass."

"What is it?"

(Fifth-grader) "Some kids fighting."

I stood there figuratively pissing in my pants and Baby Brother making noises like a champion, he was so sure of himself he even pitied me a little. "I asked you for it. . . . You Big Headed Sonofabitch, now you'll get it," this was his battle cry and he added a new phrase, "I'm going to box your ears."

He doubled up his huge fists. . . .

"Come on, mix it up, are you guys chicken?"

"Give it to him, Baby Brother."

"Yeh, Baby Brother, give it to him."

"Come on, Knees," said the cripple boy.

"Shut up before I paste you, you limpy-leg dumby," I said.

I narrowed my eyes as I had seen people do and doubled my fists; I felt brave, and true, and clean, and all-Americanish. Not this time, I thought, Jo-Jo has been giving me lessons, I'm going to surprise them this time.

36

"Make him cry, Baby Brother," after the first couple of times I was beaten up I never cried—and that was my gem, never crying, my victory in defeat.

"Why didn't you give me the paper like I wanted, Knees? . . . You're going to get it."

The circle was getting tighter. Someone shoved me at Baby Brother. He swung at me and missed. I regained my balance—not this time, I thought, no sir, not this time. . . . I'll show this dummy. I put up my dukes; unfortunately the only picture in Jo-Jo's magazine was of a very old fighter, consequently I held my guard like Corbett, or Sullivan. Baby swung at me and I jumped back more from instinct than skill, but that made twice he had swung and hadn't touched—I backpedaled.

"Give them room."

The next swing Baby Brother grazed me a little. I shook my head exaggeratedly and made a blowing sound . . . this wasn't so hard, fighting wasn't so hard, I wiped my nose like fighters do. I put my fist out and waved it in what I hoped was a fancy jab.

"Look at old Knees go to it . . . go to it, Knees."

"Come on, Baby Brother, get him."

"Get him, Knees."

I stopped backpedaling and swung. This wasn't so . . . Baby hit me in the mouth. I meant to come up, but he was on top of me swinging. A new pain shot into my ear where he hit me. I scooted away on my knees and got to my feet before he could hit me some more. There were tears of pain in my eyes, my mouth was numb and my head was ringing.

"Look, old Knees is crying."

"I'm not," I tried to wipe my face and streaked it to beat hell.

"You are."

"Knees is crying. . . . Kneeees is crryiiiiing!"

I hadn't been. I hadn't been crying. But now I was crying in earnest; because they lied on me. I hadn't been crying. I always fought against that no matter how hard I got hit. I never cried, that was my Gem. I spent all my time fighting against crying—but that's not so strange, people often do that, keep one little bit in reserve as a buffer against the Truth: an athlete, not doing his best so he could believe if he had tried his best he could have won; a thief, taking everything from a person except carfare so that he can say to himself, "See, I'm not so bad. . . . I left carfare, I could have taken that too"; a husband, patting himself on the back because he never tells his mistress that he loves her; or me, I always told myself, "I never cry so I'm not really losing"—but then I was crying and I forgot the lessons Jo-Jo had taught me. All I knew was I had lost my Gem and it didn't matter any more, nothing mattered—that rotten sonofabitch, Baby Brother, all those rotten dumb bunnies. I started windmilling my arms, Baby Brother, all of them had made me cry. My nose was snotty and I was really fighting, not as you learn to fight by experience, but simply twirling my arms as fast as I could. It was said that the best sword fighter in France had nothing to fear from the second best sword fighter in France, or something like that, but to beware the peasant who had never even seen a sword before. That is the way it was in second grade, I suppose, Baby Brother who was the third best fighter didn't have to worry about Shelley who was the fourth best fighter, or Topper who was the fifth, but I was so ignorant he couldn't defend himself. Baby began to give way. Without realizing it he backed toward the edge of the circle. Someone gave him a push back toward the center and

38

he came sprawling off balance toward me right into my spinning fists. He went down and a roar that seemed to shake the sky went up from the circle.

"Come on, Knees."

I had learned my lesson about being fancy, nose-wiping and backpedaling. I just kept swinging my arms wildly, leaning over Baby Brother really giving it to him. Baby Brother tried to get up, but I kept him down really giving it to him. . . . Bamm, bamm, bif—boy, I was really giving it to him. Suddenly I began to float in the air. If I hadn't been so busy keeping Baby Brother down I might have noticed the crowd had scattered away. My mother had me and she was shaking me crying at me, "Is this what I'm raising you to be, just another hoodlum, is that what your father, poor man, kills himself in the tailor shop for . . . for you to fight in the streets? I'm a little late and here you are fighting. Wait until I tell your Aunt Carol, she will be heartbroken." She sat me down and jerked my arm almost out of its socket dragging me home.

It took them a while to catch on to my style, even when they did I was never low man in the class again. Now, whenever I see two boys fighting in the street, I hurry past—even though I feel guilty, as if I was letting somebody down. Sometimes though I remember how I felt and I stop to break them up, but I see everyone standing around the circle enjoying themselves and urging them on and I find myself saying, what-the-hell, it's just two kids letting off steam . . . makes men of them . . . after a while I relax and start enjoying it too, maybe even urging them on.

"Use the old one-two . . . one-two!"

The next day I paid for my graduation. The bigger boys grabbed me and searched me and finding only a lead pencil, which they didn't dare destroy, one took the eraser off, pissed on it, and stuck it back on my pencil and warned me not to tell—now that type of treatment seems worse than it did then, then I thought of it as inevitable like the seasons, or going to bed by eight-fifteen, or my mother's vigil.

4

If I·THINK IN TERMS of lessons learned, or if I am in a
new situation and need an axiom, or attitude, or something by way of a guide my mind turns, not to formal
school, but to my dad's tailor shop (long since sold).
There against the backdrop of my dad's place I became
aware of my sphere of knowledge and began to plug the
holes of ignorance. Each time I filled a gap I thought,
"This is it, now I know everything about everything."
Sometimes I would go for months without noticing another hole and sometimes it was only a matter of a day,
or an hour.

It was there, in the tailor shop, that my practical
education in the life work of a man (I was assured at
the time by the Professor and Sammy), putting it to the
chicks, began in earnest. It began on the day that

Sammy came to work for my Dad. It was almost Easter, yet it was still pretty cold. Sammy had a round, nice-looking face and sometimes when he shaved small bumps would come out on his neck and chin; he had a chubby rear and a pot gut, just a small one it was not offensively large (if you can imagine an unoffensive pot gut, it actually favored him) and he always talked about getting back down to fighting weight, a hundred and thirty-five—shit yes, man, feel that arm. Sammy wasn't big, but at the time he belonged to the world of giants and herculean strength that boys are apt to lump all men into. The things I have described about Sammy I noticed after he had been around a while. Try as I might, all I can really remember of the first day that he came to work in the tailor shop is his voice floating over my head, yes sirring my dad—Yes Sir, Yes Sir and the way he looked from the knees down; his coat was longer than they were wearing them that year and below his coat he wore greenish-blue striped pants with brown socks and brown shoes—almost hickified, but stopping just short of that and being instead snappy, new, and smart.

Dad had hired Sammy because of the Professor, who was getting slower each year. The Prof proudly came from the old school. Yes, sir, a tailor was really a tailor in those days none of this botching clothing together the way they do now. The young guys that call themselves tailors couldn't work a day as a tailor when he was a young man, you had to learn your trade then. Sometimes a cheap customer would explain in the circumlocutory language of the stingy—(shrugging) Oh, this is just an old pair I'm just trying to stretch out a little, hit 'em a lick, or (laughing) heh, heh, I'm in a rush for this just . . . (insignificant motions with the

42

hands) slap it together for me (more motions). If the cheap customer was talking to the Professor he was wasting his breath, because botching was something the Prof never could, or would permit himself. Tailoring is like an art, he always said. Yes Sir, that's just what it is, an art. The Professor worked on every customer's suit like he was a duke, or something.

Also the Professor was anti-everything and a great talker. I used to pray for him when I said my prayers. The Prof would stand up, put a foot on his chair, take off his glasses, put his other hand on to something to steady himself, and show the evil of: tobacco, which he said was treated with morphine to make it habit forming; God, which was a lot of poppykaush kept up by wallstreet to keep the poor ignorant working man poor and ignorant; labor unions, "Ruined me the devils, I built that business with my own hands and those dogs ruined me . . . I'd kill everyone of them." He talked on anything, but his favorite topics were tobacco, God, the Negro situation and how it got that way, and labor unions. The Professor was my friend (shortly after my fight with Baby Brother, Jo-Jo had been fired for loafing and helping himself to cigarette money) and until Sammy came he was my sole counselor in plugging the holes that I noticed upon my sphere of knowledge from time to time.

Sammy was a "botcher," because of this fact plus his youth, he was only a third as old as the Prof, plus a keen objectivity about the quality of work a customer wanted done, he was four times faster than the Professor. But there was no rivalry between them. Each was happy in his little realm and parentally indulgent of the other—Sammy in his world of speed and efficiency and the Prof in his world of artistry and precision.

The first real indication I had of a hole in my sphere, that would plague me for years and that I later learned to call sex, was when I was seven or eight. Sometimes I wasn't even sure such a hole existed. The main difficulty was it was very hard for me to be sure of what I knew, or didn't know. Maybe grownups talk that way, spelling words. Maybe they stop laughing and look funny when anybody walks in—a child has no ruler with which to fortify and gauge his knowledge. Anyway, one time the situation got so critical that it couldn't be bluffed through and I was on the brink of a great revelation, but my Mother stepped in and whisked me to safety. At the time we lived upstairs, two floors above the tailor shop and I was allowed to hang around the business in the evenings. It's better than having him outside playing with those ruffians, picking up their language and heaven only knows what. It was almost closing time one evening when a drunk lady dancer came in and wanted to be fitted for a pair of slacks. The Prof was very educated and polite, yes madaming and of course I understand miss, with your figure it will be no problem if you will pardon my saying so, and harrumph, harrumphing all over the place.

"Of course, Madam, you understand it . . . um, um harumph . . . it is difficult to get the correct . . . um harrumph measurement for a woman, using um, um just the waist band harumph . . . but," the Professor said. (This was Prof's way of telling her she should be measured in the crotch, too.)

"Oh, hell," she said. "I haven't time to go back and piss around putting on slacks. Excuse me, Sonny," she said catching sight of me. "Go ahead and measure me, Mister."

"Harrumph . . . of course, Madam, it is best . . . we

44

wish to satisfy, of course," Prof said. He began to work his hand with the tape measure under her skirt. His corner jaw muscles were straining violently to keep from grinning, he always tried to appear stern and businesslike with customers.

"Wait just a Goddamn minute," the lady said, getting a little worked up in the struggle to spraddle her legs enough to allow Prof's hand passage up her skirt. The Professor stopped, withdrew his hand, and began fumbling with his glasses. "Oh, hell. Excuse me, Son," she said, "I'll take this damn thing off, but I haven't . . ." At that moment my mother who had been pinning on cleaning tags grabbed me and carried me upstairs.

As I grew older Prof began interpreting opera duets for me that we would chance to hear on the radio before someone had time to change the station. "What are they saying, Prof?" I would ask.

"He's asking can he come up and visit her when her folks are asleep."

"What are they saying now?"

"He's telling her he bets she's got a pretty thing," Prof explained.

(thing?)

Occasionally he would talk about his boyhood. I was a rascal when I was just a little bit older than you are now. Chris would ask my mother could they take care of me. My mother was away quite a bit . . . people weren't suspicious like they are now, and I was a cute boy. Those big girls would hug me to their breasts and pull and kiss me. Prof would stop and make a face of extreme pleasure, squinching up his eyes behind his rimless glasses and hugging his vest. This is how my education stood when Sammy came to work at the shop and I got to know him.

45

My dad was intensely interested in what he called basic economics and whenever he got the chance he lectured anyone, especially me, on the virtue of the dollar. You know why the white man gets ahead?—he saves his money. He isn't fooled with baseball games and other trifles . . . I never saw one in my life. Why should I, who cares whose batting is up, or down? All those fools talking about big league . . . the big league, they don't even have Negroes on their teams. Dad would lean close to me. Tend to business . . . not so much chin-music. These guys that work for me, even the Professor with all his ed..ed..education, waste money, he's got to have a twenty-dollar hat and the best underwear. Where'll they be in ten years, or the rest of their life . . . repairing, pressing, cleaning clothes . . . and they never get a dime ahead. When you were going to be born I didn't have a job. I might have got on the road like Stoker, but I wanted to be my own boss. Dad would put one of his huge hands on one of my puny shoulders. I borrowed your grandmother's iron and opened a pressing shop. When you were born, Son, I said you'd never go hungry even if I had to steal. As I grew older Dad was a little shy about kissing me and I, of course, was always embarrassed, but sometimes he would bend his towering face to mine and give me a young girl-like brush on the forehead and squeeze my shoulder. Look at Stoker and those fellows still working on the road and they made good money right through hard-times . . . what have they got to show for it?— nothing, but they like to be big sports. Stoker is a big whist player, now I like a game of cards as well as anyone, but if you have a family you look out for them. Where would you be, where would the business be if I ran to card tour . . . tour . . . tournaments, or the racetrack? That's where the white man gets it on us, he learns basic economics . . . basic economics . . . how to save his money. We've got to have this and that for Easter. The shock of my life came when I first saw a white person waste money, it was as if God had refuted the Blood of the Lamb.

As soon as I was old enough I started to work for my dad. I was paid a regular weekly salary and I put half of the money into a bank account Dad started for me and I kept the other half for spending money. Except for the dime I put into the Sunday school collection plate and the Hershey bars I guiltily bought myself, the spending money went into a box under my bed marked BUSINESS CAPITOL. I had a small business of my own. Near the end of the week some of the help ran short of cash and I would loan them lunch money on interest. No one wanted to ask my dad for an advance the second time, not that he would have refused, but because they would have had to listen to a lecture on basic economics. I learned a lot from my business. The shop wasn't big and I knew all the guys, but I knew them deeper than simply to say hello. I knew them as you only get to know a person when you loan him your money. Sammy became one of my steady customers. He and the Professor, who was the only person who never borrowed from me, were the best pals I can remember.

Sammy was a lover and it wasn't long after he started working at the tailor shop that various ladies began to come around to see him. If my dad was there they pretended to be on business. Dad always made it clear —this is a place of business, not so much chin-music. To me he would add—Son, when a customer comes in jump, never leave the customer waiting. Learn all the prices, so you can tell the customer how much without looking it up . . . speak. He shouldn't have to go to the Jew down the street to get service.

One day Sammy said to me, after a little thin woman who had been making eyes and pushing up against him while he sewed, had left, "You see her?"

"Who?" I asked.

"That little skinny one that was just in here."

"Yes."

"It's little ones like that . . ."

"Like what?" I interrupted.

"Like that . . . they usually got a box so big you need to tie a two by four across your butt to keep from falling in."

I nodded sagely.

In the meantime the Professor's stories were getting less vague—these girls would talk my mother into letting me spend the night with them. They would fondle my private parts and get my little thing so upset I wouldn't be good for a day. Sammy, not to be outdone, would tell a story—we were coming back from swimming, walking down the railroad tracks. She said she had to stop and not for me to look. She went around a bush. I waited and then went around, too. She had her pants down p p-ing. She let me look at it and then we did it to each other . . . she grew up to be real fine, too.

As a sort of bonus when I loaned the fellows money I would go to the Greasy-Spoon, the Bar-B-Q Pit, or to Walgreen's to get their lunch for them. One day I had gone to the store for the presser and when I came back Thelma, a big woman that would hang around Sammy sometimes when his wife or my Dad weren't there, was talking to Sammy.

Sammy got up from his machine as I went past carrying the presser his lunch. "Come in the back with me while I iron out this coat seam," he said to Thelma.

I gave the presser his food and went back to the front of the shop and sat down.

"Hey, Ed, come here," Sammy called to me. His voice was muffled by bags of clothing. The shop was crowded with garments, pants, shirts, dresses, etc., hung everywhere. The tailors' ironing space was a little nook completely hidden from the front by two rows of bagged garments and surrounded on three sides by clothing.

"What do you want?" I yelled.

"Come here."

When I went back Sammy had finished ironing the seam and he had started playing around in the top of Thelma's dress.

My eyes felt as if they were burning.

"Oh, Sammy, stoppp . . . you're terrible. Look, that little boy is looking at you," the lady said.

"Who? That's my buddy. Come here, Ed, come here."

I wanted to go to him, but I was embarrassed. I wanted to go closer, but I wanted to be invisible.

"Don't Sammy," she whined.

"Oh, shut up, girl," Sammy bullied and teased her. He pulled the brassiere down off her shoulders and pulled out her big slightly pendulous breasts. "Hey, Ed."

"Oh, Sammy," she whined, "You're the worst . . . Oh, Sammy, stop."

He put her right breast in his mouth, kissing it and rolling his eyes. "Hey, Ed," he beckoned me closer.

"Awww, Sammy," is all I could seem to say.

"Come here," he coaxed, "and look at them."

49

If I could have only disappeared and still have been there. I wondered and feared if they knew about the warmness in my pants. I had inched within grabbing distance and Sammy reached out and clutched me and pulled me to them. He took my hand and placed it on her free breast. I stood there wanting to sink through the floor holding her body. The woman had stopped pleading and watched me curiously. Sammy took my other hand and pushed it in on her dress, right where her legs met and her stomach pushed out a little. I still had her breast.

"Kiss it," he urged. I kissed her breast a tentative peck all atremble.

"No, Stupid, not there . . . Thelma, help him," Sammy said. She lifted up her breast from the bottom and shoved it at me curiously. The teat loomed at me like a knuckle of a child's fist, or the eye of a drunk. Then, keplunk it was in my mouth. She rubbed me between the pant legs. The shop began to swim and I braced myself against the twirl of the place by wrapping my knees around one of her legs. Sammy hiked up her dress and directed my hand under it. We almost upset a clothes rack full of overcoats stored for the coming summer, and she let me try for the laugh. While I was at it Sammy kept laughing and she kept laughing and Sammy was screaming something in my ear and the universe opened up until I thought I knew everything about everything.

5

THREE TIMES IN MY LIFE my dad was buddy-buddy with me. Oh, he was buddy-buddy in an advice giving way, but for a long time I didn't think of my father— I guess the only word for it is human—as a human being. I guess my dad wanted to be a balancing influence in my life and through his eyes, including most of the immediate family, I was surrounded by shortsighted clowns. To offset the good-timers he gave me a lot of advice about politics and economics and the future. My dad always began lectures to me with, "You won't understand this now, Son, but (nod, nod) try to remember what I tell you." If you look at the forest as a whole Dad's analyses of things were pretty accurate; however, he was under the Professor's influence and everything wrong he attributed to the gullibility of the colored races of the world and to a group of wicked millionaires. Maybe my father wasn't trying to be a balancing influence in my life; maybe he was just lonesome for someone to listen to him when he talked. Perhaps it was both reasons—anyways if I had had to depend on my dad to teach me, I might never have learned to laugh.

One Sunday when I was very little I climbed into bed with my father and got on his chest.

"Hi there, Big Guy," he said to me.

"Hi, Sir," I said.

My mother always razzed me about calling my dad sir. "Boy, oh, Boy! When he's around you toe the mark," she would say, half kidding and half spitefully serious.

I looked down at the little holes on my dad's face where his whiskers came out. My mother was in the kitchen baking and singing along with the choir on the radio. When the biscuits were ready she would call my dad and he would get up and go butter them and then we would sit down and eat.

"Sir, did you have any fights when you were a boy?" I asked. Were you a boy, I thought.

My father smiled at me. "Once," he said.

"What did you do, Sir?"

"This bully kept picking on me . . . every chance he got. I knew that he was stronger than me and he kept after me. Finally one day I scooped up some sawdust and threw it in his eyes and he never bothered me after that."

It was a fine story, but pretty short so I began to stretch it out.

"How old were you, Sir?"

"I don't know . . . maybe twelve."

"He never bothered you after that?"

"No, never . . . we became friends after that."

"Did he go to school with you?"

"We d..d..didn't go to school. We worked in the mill together."

"What else did you do when you were a boy?"

"Worked, Son. Worked."

"All the time, Sir?"

He lay there a long time not saying anything. Maybe he's dead, I thought. I leaned over close to his face and squinted at his whiskers to see if they were growing the way dead people's were supposed to. Then he answered me.

"Well . . . well, once I was fishing with a line tied around my big toe and an alligator grabbed the line and before I knew it I was in the water. He tried to eat me, but I was too fast for him . . . I straddled his back and stuck my fingers in his eyes. If you ever want to beat an alligator who is trying to eat you, stick your fingers in his eyes . . . the pain drives him wild and he'll take you to the closest shore."

That was my first talk about nothing with my dad—we talked quite often, as I said, but except for the story about the alligator his talks always led somewhere, there was always a fable, or moral behind one of his lectures. "We stopped off every evening and shot a game of pool . . . one day I was late and Junior went ahead. When I got to the pool hall there was a big cr..cr..crowd and Junior was laying on the floor between two tables dead, with a bullet in his head. He had just been sitting there watching the games, waiting for me, when two men started arguing and one of them pulled a gun and started shooting at the other and hit Junior instead . . . (moral) it's better to stay away from those kind of places." Or, "An old doctor told me once, (moral) never marry a woman whose father is a drunkard. I learned a lot from that doctor. A good friend of mine—years ago, married a wonderful young lady, she didn't drink herself, but her father was a drunkard. They had two children, a boy and a girl, and today both of them are in the nut house from just plain drinking."

That little Sunday morning chat had to suffice for a long time as my glimpse of my Dad being buddy-buddy. One memory is not too much to go on for six years and my dad floated up to the heights of Mount Olympus as far as being a human being went.

The second time my dad was buddy-buddy with me two big things happened: he descended Olympus permanently, and I stopped thinking of him as an "old" person. I don't mean that I didn't realize he was grown —I guess I realized that the Prof and Sammy were grown, too—what I actually mean is he began to have validity for me. Older people were simply rule-makers, and they flitted through my life giving orders much as a bossy ghost might do in a haunted English castle; I hardly even thought of them as personalities and it never occurred to me that there was any correlation between the way they acted and their being part of all they had met.

For instance the principal where I graduated from grade school, I never thought of him as being anything but the principal. Oh sure, maybe he walked four miles to school after delivering newspapers and all that, but in my mind, when I thought about it, he was still the principal: a grown man shrunken to the size of a boy delivering papers; fighting the battle of the bulge at his waistline and losing his hair. I never visualized him wanting to stop and climb a tree or shoot marbles. Old people were lumped with everything else I didn't understand and hadn't gotten around to exploring: the metric system; how chickens did it; why corned beef tasted different; what held airplanes in the air—once I conducted an experiment from a junior scientist series that I was taking by mail, I was to blow across a piece of curled paper and watch its tendency to rise, this was supposed to illustrate how planes stay in the air.

I conducted the experiment all right, but I didn't really understand it. Later I discovered the shape of the wing, the camber, supports the plane in the air and later too I learned that past experiences defend and support people. I didn't know that then, and to me they were all (planes in the sky and older people's actions) suspended in space without any visible means of support. The time when my dad caught up with my cousin and I and passed us I realized what a big strong man he was and I thought of how much life he must have seen and suddenly he became a reality, a human being to me.

It was an evening in the Fall, my dad, my Cousin Ralph, and I were driving back to the tailor shop after making some deliveries and we took a shortcut through the park. In retrospect it seems as if the temperature was perfect for Chicago in the Fall and that it was not quite dark, but deep, deep twilight.

We came to a place where in summer gangs played baseball, and my Dad pulled over to the curb and stopped the delivery truck.

"I'm going to let you boys stretch your legs," he said.

We got out of the truck and stood on the grass, just then the street lights began to glow.

"Did you see the lights come on?" my cousin asked.

I nodded.

"Are you guys just going to stand there?" my Dad said. My cousin and I shouted at the darkness and began to run. The grass stretched before us an eternity long. I turned my head to challenge my cousin and I could see the delivery truck and my dad standing by the door on the driver's side watching us.

"Let's go, I'll race you," I shouted to my cousin. We poured on the steam. We were running against a breeze and the wind roared in our ears. I had on a jacket and it filled with air and puffed out behind. I imagined to myself how grown up I must have looked. Running with your jacket puffing out seemed the height, the pinnacle of adulthood. Suddenly something was behind us—it was my dad—my dad went past us running so fast, faster than anyone I had ever seen before. He ran until he was almost out of sight and then he stopped and waited for us. When we got to him my cousin and I shouted and asked him to run some more.

"No, no more, boys. I'm tired," he said.

"How'd you learn to run so fast, Sir?" I asked.

"Work, Big Guy, hard work."

The third time my dad was buddy-buddy with me was when he told me about playing policy.

Policy is a semi-illegal game, similar to lottery. You bet on a combination of numbers and symbols and if your combination comes up you win. No bet is too small, you can even play a nickel and when you win the return is fabulous, but on the other hand the odds against you are terrific. The selection of a combination is an art in itself. Some people add up the numbers on car license plates, some play hunches, others get theirs in dreams, some simply play the same combination day after day, year after year, hoping the law of averages will catch up with them—they are all spurred on by stories of nick-of-time wealth. I have imagined a lot of things, but I never imagined my father playing policy, not even in my biggest dream.

"Guy," my dad said, we had been discussing business. "I had just started the pressing shop . . . It had been going for a month . . . at first business was very slow, but toward the end of the month it began to gradually pick up and I knew if I could hang on I could make it go. The rent was due on the shop and I didn't have the money. Your mother was going to the hospital any day too, to have you. One of the regular customers that came into the shop sold policy—you know how it is when you're in business, you have to accommodate your customers . . . and from time to time I would put a nickel on a number. A nickel was a lot of money in those days, but it was good advertisement. 'Big Ed's a regular fellow,' he would say . . . and that's good business . . . a..accommodate your customers. Anyway, Son, the night before the rent was due I went home very tired. That night a strange thing happened, I dreamed a combination in my sleep and I got up in the middle of the night and wrote it down. Your mother and I had one dollar, I took half of that, 50 cents—I never will forget it was on a Thursday. When the policy man came around pestering me to play a nickel I put the whole half dollar on the number I had dreamed. (nod, nod) That same afternoon the landlord came around for the rent money. I told him I didn't have it, but I would have it the next day—and I did. When he came back the next day I had the money. My combination had hit! I won over a hundred dollars. . . . I paid him and I bought groceries and baby things and a steam iron with the rest of the money."

Just those three times.

Yet even those times I don't think it was the story-book kind of father-son relationship. You know, "Here, Son . . . you throw the old pigskin like this."

6

WHEN I WAS IN SEVENTH GRADE, I was a rabid fan of a game that was popular in our group called the dozens. The game sprang up during the summer between sixth and seventh grade and by the time school started we were all connoisseurs. Looking back the game seems to have been symbolic and restrained and very regimented —that's now, then it seemed natural and spontaneous and free. Now, too, I realize the dozens is a traditional game, but at the time we assumed the game was our idea. We were normal children, conceited; innocently positive that everything we were rediscovering was new; but our naïveté served a purpose, it protected us from self-consciousness that probably would have frozen our imaginations and bound us; not realizing the sacred antiquity, or enormity of our discoveries we revised and twisted, reshaping the ideas and symbols, the truths of the world into forms that we could dig.

Day after day, at recess, going and coming from school, on Saturdays any time that we had a chance we would play the dozens. The idea was to make your opponent lose his temper or cry, to try and drag him down by belittling him and his relations. You didn't jump right into the dozens first there was a prelude of signifying. Two guys would start hinting about each other's relatives and we would gather around them forming a ring. The hinting would get stronger and stronger and then they would start playing the dozens. Whenever a person said something sharp it was considered a score and we usually all yelled, "Score," pantomiming the action of giving a point by wetting a finger and drawing an imaginary line in the air. Marking score wasn't really too important though, because the winner, like a modern beauty queen, was decided by a great many things; poise, rapidity of comeback, quality of comeback, ability to hold your temper and the number of guys rooting for you. No one ever counted the score as a means of determining the winner— Victory was confused, it was an overall, intangible thing; there were times when both guys thought they had won, other times when each was sure he had lost; we marked points simply for the enjoyment of participating, just as audiences used to sing the words to songs as they were flashed upon the screen in old movie houses.

After the preamble of signifying was over and the bad talk really began the roles of the winner and loser became rigid. The two cats inside the ring would drag each other without mercy. The guy who was winning at the moment would be bullying with terrible remarks the guy who was losing. The loser in turn seemed to be paying no attention whatsoever, or only polite, token interest. The loser just stood around taking the insults as best he could trying to look off-handed and pretending unconcern. The theory was that the loser could reduce the effectiveness of the winner's insults by assuming an attitude of indifference. The winner's attitude of bravado was accepted among us as proper behavior and the best method to break through the loser's assumed indifference. Bravado was not just bragging, or insolence; it was an attitude completely dedicated and calculated to get under your rival's skin, depress and aggravate, inflame and intimidate him. The losing cat would stand there muttering, "Un hunh," "Yes," or "You know WHO," (The "Who" supposedly someone in his opponent's immediate family, preferably the mother) stalling for time hoping to figure out a sharp comeback to change the tide; in the meantime the winner would hammer away trying to get his opponent by some sign to show his defeat. We all agreed on the basic roles of the winner and loser; however, everyone made changes on these styles according to his personal idea of effectiveness.

You were also permitted to borrow freely from anybody's material and if someone came up with a new rhyme:

I saw your sister cuttin' through the field,
Slipping and slidin' like an automobile,
She didn't shoot seven, she didn't shoot eleven,
That dirty sonofabitch can't go to heaven.

or score:

*If my dog had a face like yours I'd shave his ass and
make him walk backward.*

by the next day you would hear another cat using it.
The punch of the dozens, the power lay in the rhymes
and scores and comebacks, but the trick of success, the
latitude for individual expression, the thread between
genius and mediocrity, was in the presentation.

The biggest fear I can remember from those days was
the poor opinion of the rest of the guys. I think we were
all haunted by the specter of acceptance. When you are
grown eight, or nine, people seldom constitute a world
—then it was everything. This need to be-a-part gave
the dozens its strength and stature and made it a terribly large section of our lives; luckily in our group, except for Joe and L.D. who were our champs and lost
only to each other, we were pretty well matched and
took turns at the bottom.

Surely inside the players there glowed the semi-
instinctive ember of combat and in the winner there
was the spark of victory, but the combative instinct or
the pride of victory were insignificant brush fires com-
pared to the raging inferno of terror we all felt when
we thought of losing. The terror was so strong even with
victory practically assured the winning boy was afraid,
so strong the loser endured any humiliation, trying indifference, agreement, anything to postpone defeat. The
most terrifying moment of childhood was the first time
a dozens player lost a scoring session, some carried the
experience into adulthood never completely recovering
from the swirling emotions, or the glimpse into the
foolish pit of eternity that came when they had lost and
stood alone. It felt so funny an odd, red, and salt tast-
ing, and mother wanting—suddenly the faces of the

circle seemed to grow hostile, their laughter encouraging the opposition against you—the other guy scoring, scoring, looking for an insult so vehement there could be no indifference, or agreement. The loser trying not to show his anger, or humiliation and the gang waiting for his wall to crack—for him to cry, or try to fight, to show his defeat so they could howl all the m ore, each, I think, remembering his time, his defeat in the circle.

During this time, in seventh grade, there was a new boy named Paul who failed with us. It didn't enter my mind at the time, but, now, sometimes when I sit down to stroke my beard I find myself wondering what happened. I like to feel superior to the past; perhaps not have it down pat, but having at least a good insight into what has gone on. I like to say to myself I should have done it this way instead of that; here is where his strength lay, right here, or such and such went wrong there, or they did exactly right under the circumstances, etc. Anyway, with Paul I don't know what went wrong —maybe nothing went wrong at all. Maybe he was too weak, or too good, or he had a mannerism that rubbed us the wrong way, maybe the game itself was inherently at fault.

The new boy's big day, the first day he was pulled into the dozens with us began with Joe baiting L.D. into a game. Joe interrupted L.D. who was talking. "Quiet, Son," Joe said. Joe and L.D., as I said, were the best players in our group and we thought they were probably the best in the whole world. None of the rest of us had ever beaten them and we would have backed them against anyone. To us they were infallible (although L.D. was a little better than Joe) our champions, our Jesuses, the kings of the seventh grade.

"Where did, You, get that son 3-6-9?" L.D. asked.

That was what Joe was waiting for and he slipped L.D. into the dozens rhyming on him.

I don't call you son 'cause you shine,
I call you son 'cause you're mine.

We roared with laughter. Later, as the game progressed and someone began to lose we would not even dare to smile. It was considered legitimate for the person who lost to try and salvage his prestige by challenging someone standing around the circle to a game of the dozens. The only thing you had to do to be eligible was to smile, or just seem to be enjoying yourself.

If you grin, you're in,

was the rule. So we would stand trying to hold our faces solemnly. Instead of depressing us the struggle to appear somber intensified the game—scores, rhymes, vulnerability, belonging, they were all scrambled up, defiant and fearful—laughing, marking score, standing around the ring—we assumed an insolent air, "Here," it said, "don't pull me into your two-bit game, I know too much shit for you guys." The guy who lost would look around the circle trying to find someone he could beat and each heart would tighten with fear. Everyone was equal, leaders varied with the game, or activity and because of this no cat would turn down a challenge, there wasn't anyone in the group who bought brotherhood by strange antics, or servility, there were no outside-insiders in the gang. We would argue and fight and call each other horrible names, but except for when we played the dozens we were just testing our skill and we pulled our punches. If a fellow was fat he might be called pea-head, or big ears, but never fatty. If a guy was snaggled-tooth he might be called skinny, or have any of his lesser defects magnified, but he was never called a snag-gled-tooth bastard—you don't have to be a genius to figure out what a person is real sensitive about. Since then I have revolved in other orbits that were the op-posite, they didn't bark, but the cruelty of the things they said in the most sugary manner was much worse than the filthy yelling we did in the seventh grade. When we played the dozens it was a different matter, nothing was sacred. Nothing was sacred—that was the glory of it—if your mother was cross-eyed she was called cross-eyed. Joe's mother was fat with a potbelly and L.D., who was winning, said to him,

Your Mammy got so many wrinkles on her belly she has to screw her draws on.

In the dozens no quarter was asked, or given. When the loser looked around the circle for a victim we all trem-bled, thinking to ourselves suppose he slips me into the dozens and I have to play and I lose.

Paul's day, even though he had started the game Joe lost; however, he wasn't worried he was sure that he could beat one of us to patch things up. He looked around the ring for an opponent; we all, except the new boy, tried to assume an air of being somewhere else. At the time I thought Paul didn't know the rules of the dozens because he seemed to be inviting trouble. There was no immunity in the dozens, any person who stood around the ring was in the danger of being slipped into the game. If you were too good to have your parents talked about you had no right to listen and enjoy some-one else's defeat, "If you don't swim stay away from the water." Paul was standing next to me grinning. Joe turned slowly around the circle looking at us. When he got to Paul he stopped—for a moment I thought he was looking at me.

"Hey, Boy, what're you grinning at?" Joe said.

For a second I felt sorry for Paul.

Paul didn't answer.

The circle was quiet.

"Say, Son, I'm talking to you," Joe said.

"Me?" Paul asked.

"You, SON," Joe said.

"Son?" Paul said, acting innocent.

"Yeh, Son."

Paul didn't talk like the rest of us. At first I couldn't figure out what was different. Then suddenly I realized we had southern accents and he didn't. That was a funny thing we never teased each other about our down home accents, even when we played the dozens. Maybe it's not so funny though, I mean, you haven't time to go around checking and testing everything to see if you are taking it for granted; in fact, some things you would just never question even if you did test them, they seem so universal: like clothes, then maybe one day you read a *National Geographic* and there is some far off native girl standing butt-naked for the cameraman not trying to hide herself, or anything, not even looking as if she knows she is doing wrong the way they do in the pinup books. Paul's voice so unlike ours scratched the guilty and angry and helpless feelings we had toward—I guess toward the South, feelings that we had acquired along with our accents from our parents. We had all been told the story of the man who wished he was white and one day fell into a vat of lye, so we didn't want to be white, but we were sad that our folks were not the men and women in the advertisements and that we were not the boys in the Saturday serials and that we could not grow up to be cowboys, or stunt pilots.

"I don't play that," Paul said.

"Don't play what?" Joe asked.

"The dozens," Paul said. He knew about the dozens.

"Why not?" Joe said. He smiled around the circle at us and we smiled back at him, unafraid now that the victim had been chosen. We stood waiting for Joe to chew Paul up. Joe usually lost to L.D., but he could beat any of the rest of us easily and we never doubted he could beat the new boy.

"I just don't," Paul said.

"Why not?" Joe said again.

Paul didn't answer.

"Why not, Son?" Joe repeated. Joe was really getting mad. We watched him reverently.

"Why don't you play the dozens? If you don't swim, Son," Joe said, "stay away from the water."

Paul smiled and then he started rhyming on Joe.

> *I don't play the dozens 'cause the dozens are bad,*
> *But I can tell you how many children your*
> *Granma had.*

Paul knew the dozens all right. He was the best player we had ever heard. He beat Joe worse than any of us had ever been beaten. Joe got angry, but Paul laughed and kept right on scoring.

> *Oh, shut up, Boy, you're just mad because you'll*
> *never be the man your mother is.*

L.D. tried to jump in to help Joe, but Paul was also too good for him. Paul told him,

> *Get away, from me, ugly child, . . . your breath smells like wild oxfarts.*

Paul beat them both, but we did not laugh—in seventh grade, even then we had our idols and we hated to modify, or change gods. At any age it is disconcerting to realize the last word is fallible.

After that for a month Paul was king of the dozens. We didn't like him—maybe it all happened too fast, maybe he should have worked his way up through the ranks, or something.

One day he got sick and was out of school for a week. In our school when a student missed more than three days he had to bring one of his parents back with him when he reentered school. When Paul returned to school he brought his mother, whom none of us had ever seen before with him.

The morning that Paul came back to school it was very foggy. We were waiting for the first bell and he and his mother suddenly loomed out of the mist walking together and holding hands like lovers. Paul's mother was a big heavyset woman. She was wearing a gray coat and with her free hand she held a handkerchief up to her face as if she had a toothache or a bad cold or pneumonia or something. When they got to the school door Paul tried to open it with his free hand, but it was stuck. His mother gave it a hard tug with one, then with both her hands and it opened. When she took the handkerchief down for a second to tug the door we saw that she didn't have a nose, nothing just two gaping holes.

Of course once we found out his mother didn't have a nose Paul was done for. At recess we were busy getting ready, then at lunch going home Joe got Paul into a game.

"Hey, Son," Joe said, baiting Paul, "where you been?"

"I'm not your son, I'm your pa," Paul said. Then he opened up and began to rhyme on Joe.

> *General Mac was a fighting man,*
> *He did it to your ma with a gun in his hand.*

Joe stood around and took it for a while to bait him more, then he reached into his pocket. (This was a pre-arranged signal.) Joe pulled out his handkerchief and put it across the bottom of his face.

"Hynh?" he said. "I couldn't understand you . . . my cold you know."

Paul didn't move. Everyone who had a handkerchief put it up to his face like Joe. We coughed and sneezed to beat hell, the way Paul's mother did, pretending we had pneumonia, or something the way she did. The other guys without handkerchiefs pushed their noses back with their hands until all you could see were holes.

"Your mother . . ." Paul began again.

"Whaat?" Joe interrupted. "My cold you know."

Paul began to cry.

We roared with laughter.

After that whenever Paul came around all you had to do was to take out a handkerchief, or just reach for your pocket and he'd beat it. He began to play hooky a lot and they had to send him to reform school and he stayed there until he graduated and went to high school.

7

THE YEARS BETWEEN twelve and fifteen were very
mixed up for me, everything was a mathematical hodge-
podge of motivations and aspirations and frustrations
which interconnected, criss-crossed, and overlapped—
but there was one constant in the equation of life I was
trying to iron out, or rather trying to iron me out and
that constant was the Boy Scouts. The scouts thumped
through my life like the beat of the military bands we
would march to on the Fourth of July and the four/four
time of scouting, BE PREPARED, THE SCOUT
OATH, THE SCOUT LAW, THE SCOUT SONG,
tempered with past experiences, marked the cadence of
all my actions.

I marched and drilled, left flanked and right flanked
into various footpaths, or what seemed to be footpaths,

but they have since broadened into set opinions and roads of life. Also I picked up a zillion skills during that period: fire-making, hook shots, masturbation, potato peeling.

I realize men have crossed oceans in little boats and have survived terrible tortures, yet, even now, for some reason, I am unabashedly proud of my scout accomplishments; when I see a group of scouts I want to talk with them and challenge them. I want to inquire what their ranks are and ask did they ever walk seven miles without taking a swallow from their canteen. I loved the scouts. During my scouting period I was unswervingly enthusiastic, plus I had an enormous ability not to become bored with it all. When I think of the overnight hikes, for instance, I always remember them so freshly with such nostalgia it seems hard to believe I went on, maybe, fifteen or more during my scout career instead of one, or two, they never palled on me, or I never saw through them.

Our troop was sponsored by a club of local businessmen and periodically one, or two of them would come down to visit us. They would stand up in the front of the assembly room with the scoutmaster, it seemed they all wore striped suits, glasses without rims and had tan thinning hair. The scoutmaster would introduce them whereupon we would give a big skyrocket cheer; however this was not insincerity on our part, we hadn't developed to the point where we automatically despised a hand that fed us, furthermore, we were terribly anxious to please our scoutmaster whom we all liked. After the introduction the meeting would go on as usual, we would do the pledge and oath, then we would break up into patrols to work on our advancement.

I did very well in the scouts, advancementwise. I

72

reached the rank of Eagle, which is as high as you can go, and I did it in record time. There are two prerequisites to each advancement in the scouts: first, there are the conventional requirements such as knot tying and first aid; secondly, there is a tenure requirement, time in grade, as they say in the service, it is necessary to spend a certain period of time at each rank before being eligible to advance. As you progress the conventional requirements grow harder and harder, paralleling this the time in grade before you are eligible to be promoted grows continually longer. When I joined the Boy Scouts I told myself I was going to have all my conventional requirements for the next rank passed before my time in grade permitted me to be promoted, therefore, as soon as I had enough tenure I would advance—let's see, it was one week in grade for Tenderfoot, so I joined one Thursday and the next Thursday when I came back I passed my test and became a Tenderfoot. For a while the time required in grade always seemed too long and I hated the tenure prerequisite; however, before I finally reached Eagle my attitude toward the length of tenure underwent complete reversal, running the gamut from impatience at the beginning to gratefulness as the other prerequisites grew harder and more difficult to fulfill, to stark fear as the conventional requirements grew still harder and reached, it seemed to me, at least in the area of swimming, impossibility. Of course, we were always being prodded forward. Notwithstanding you could stay at Tenderfoot, or any other rank for as long as you wished; nevertheless, I was determined to stick to my schedule, I was completely sold in scouting and interpreted doing my best to doing my duty as proceeding with all deliberate speed to Eagle. Also, at the time, I was carrying the

MINORITY GROUP OUTSTANDING ACHIEVE-
MENT: THEREBY PROVING THE TRUE WORTH
OF NEGROES flag extremely conscientiously and I was
also carrying the I'M SMALLER THAN AVERAGE
BUT I CAN DO ANYTHING YOU CAN DO flag,
plus, too, a couple of others. As I said, I managed to
keep up a safe, steady pace until I reached swimming.
To be a First Class Scout you had to pass a fifty yard
swimming test—I couldn't really swim fifty yards, but I
practiced and practiced and just before my tenure requirement was fulfilled I passed the test. After First
Class you advance by merit badges through the other
ranks up to Eagle. A merit badge is a certificate of proficiency you receive when you prove your ability in a
specific field. To be an Eagle you had to have a total of
twenty-one merit badges, eleven of which you could
choose from your own preference along with ten required ones. One of the required merit badges was lifesaving—I thought I would never pass the lifesaving
merit badge, I had barely passed the simple fifty yards
swimming test for First Class.

The only time I could arrange to take the lifesaving
test was during my regular swimming class at high
school. My swimming instructor had agreed to officiate.
He blew his whistle and cleared the pool, there were
about twenty boys in my class, everyone climbed out
and stood along the sides. I gave the instructor my certificate to sign if I passed. I demonstrated a number of
strokes and dives and answered questions about lifesaving techniques. The last test was a simulated rescue;
someone was supposed to jump into the pool and act as
if they were drowning and I was supposed to go in and
get him. I looked at the swimming instructor. He was
a big man—I can't really say what he was like because

I never figured him out, all I remember is that he kept the pool very cold, we all said that he put ice cubes in the water, not that we really believed that he did, but we had picked up enough adult mannerisms to think bitching made us seem older and wiser. The instructor chose his assistant to be the drowning victim. The assistant was almost as big as the instructor, he was easily the largest boy in the class, he always gave you the impression that he was kidding you, I mean that he wasn't really a boy, but a full grown man—not that we didn't think we were full grown, but you know what I mean. The assistant jumped into the deep part and swam out to the middle. Then he started splashing around as if he were drowning. I jumped in after him and swam out to the middle. We were taught that a drowning person was dangerous and there was a regular set of steps to subdue the victim. I tried to get around behind the assistant like the rule book said, but he kept turning to face me. I grabbed at the victim and he ducked me. I grabbed at him again and he ducked me and stood on my head. I never thought he was going to let me up. He let me go. I came up slowly; I should have bounced off the bottom of the pool, but I forgot. I began to choke. The assistant ducked me some more, all the time he pretended that he was drowning and that he was hysterical with fear. I grabbed at him some more and he pushed me under, finally he let me subdue him—I was so tired, I didn't think I could make it to the edge of the pool just by myself, it looked a million yards away. I put my hands on his shoulders and he rolled over on his back. I put one hand under his chin and started flailing for shore. We didn't move. I was crying. Far away, frozen in space, I could see the instructor's feet in shower shoes and his white pants rolled up above his ankles and the naked legs of my classmates. The assistant started thrashing his legs around, I was desperate, I thought he was going to pretend he was drowning again, then I realized he was flutter kicking, helping me along—we started to move. I flailed away at the water and he kept kicking and the edge got closer and closer. When we reached the side of the pool they helped me pull him out and then I had to apply artificial respiration; my classmates gave me a skyrocket cheer and the swimming instructor laughed and laughed and signed my slip—Jesus, I loved the scouts.

Outside of super-enthusiasm and my irreverent advancement, which mounted to almost sacrilege, I was a normal scout. My favorite activity, I guess it was everyone's favorite activity, *was* an overnight hike. A few miles outside of town, seven miles, just the right distance for the required fourteen mile trek, there was a forest preserve with a scout site and we would usually hike out there.

Saturday morning we would assemble outside the clubroom with our packs slung over our shoulders; the veterans of two, or three hikes assumed the mannerisms of hardened Indian scouts, or foreign legionnaires, spitting and squinting up at the sky. We would leave in groups of two at one-minute intervals and by nine-thirty we would be strung out along the road. About three quarters of a mile outside of town Cokes, Nehis, rootbeers and Pepsi Colas began to appear. Everyone put a couple of bottles in his pack, on top, right under the flap and when we got out on the road we drank them. Your partner would go down on one knee, not taking his pack off, and you would get his drink for him, then you would kneel on one knee and he would get yours for you. Someone would always throw a bottle away

76

without concealing it, or drop one and smash it on the road and the scoutmaster would come along and give us heck, telling us that he was disappointed in us and that he felt very ashamed. After a while we would pull out semi-melted candy bars and eat them as we walked. The scoutmaster would come along and ask us if we wanted a break, but we would refuse. After a while though the scoutmaster would go to the head of the column and raise his hand, cavalry fashion, for us to halt and we would take a break. Then we would begin to walk again and someone would begin a song and it would pass down the line until we were all singing. We sang the "Marine Hymn" and the "Army Air Force Song," "Anchors Aweigh" and the one about the caissons rolling along, we sang "Six Pence" and "The Long and the Short and the Tall"—we all felt very rugged walking along with little beads of sweat on our foreheads and holding our thumbs braced under the straps of our packs to ease the seesawing bite against our shoulders. Once there was a light snow a Friday evening before we were to go on a hike; however it was decided we would go anyway and the next day as we went along the snow was melting and leaving tiny puddles and each ditch had a muddy little river scooting along its bottom . . . we talked to one another, watch that goddam puddle . . . yeh, it's slippery as hell . . . yeh, but we'll make it. We felt extra, extra tough and we hoped the war would last long enough for us to get into it—we felt about war the way soldiers always say they felt before they got into it and tried it, very romantic and patriotic. About eleven o'clock during a rest period some new guy would say we must be almost there—we weren't, we were never even halfway by eleven. I knew it, but it always pissed me off when

77

someone put it into words. I don't like to think about unpleasant things until I am over the hump, more than halfway through. The hikes weren't unpleasant—I don't mean that, if we had been offered a ride we would have refused; nevertheless we were all glad when the walking was over and we could just feel good in our achievement. Someone would tell the new guy we weren't halfway then we would all resolve not to take so many breaks and trudge on. Periodically someone would try to get a song going again, it would go spasmodically down the line and die out.

Finally we would arrive at the campsite, we would swear and toss off our packs and yell to one another by our last names; we would organize and warn one another not to goof-off. Our sleeping bags would come up in a truck and we would form a human conveyor belt and pass them down the line from arm to arm the way English soldiers did in war movies when they passed mortar shells in the desert, or blitzed refugee children.

After we unloaded the truck we would break up into patrols. On overnight hikes we were supposed to practice "patrol living," consequently most projects were conducted in that manner: we cooked, ate and slept by patrols and in games, or song fests we competed the same way.

The first time I went on an overnight hike was shortly after I joined the scouts. I had not yet decided on a patrol and I was assigned to one for the trip. Joining a patrol is roughly equivalent to joining a fraternity, or church; you can change afterward, but it is considered poor management. The patrol I was assigned to was made up of all the troop goof-offs: they were swell guys, loyal and generous, but they giggled during the serious parts of the scout ritual, they were negligent in their dues and attendance and even though they could easily pass most of the requirements they weren't very interested in advancement—in short, they were what people like to call real boys; however, it seemed to me (perhaps my analysis is distorted, because at the time I was exclusively on the side of law and order) instead of being semi-indulgent and affectionate toward the goof-offs, as tradition has it grownups are supposed to be, sort of like Tom Sawyer's Aunt Polly—the scoutmaster disliked them. Anyway, the Saturday of the hike only three members of the goof-offs showed up making them the smallest patrol so I was assigned to them.

Everyone was especially nice to me, there were only four Negroes in the troop and we enjoyed what might be called super-equality. Anyway that very first hike I began picking up all kinds of camping skills and lore and I learned to masturbate.

Masturbation was a great boon to me because except for the couple of times Sammy talked a lady into letting me warm things up for him I was left to my own devices and my devices, frankly speaking, were nonexistent.

With the hike and all we had a very busy day. When it got dark we had a brief camp fire ceremony and then we broke up into patrols again and went back to our sleeping areas to turn in. Someone said it was warmer in a sleeping bag if you didn't have on any clothing, so we all slept in our birthday suits.

The three guys in the patrol besides myself were: Smitty, Henry and Earle. Smitty was the assistant patrol leader, the patrol leader didn't come. Most of us were still pretty wishywashy and groping around for the roles we wanted to attach to our personalities and show the world, one day we were this and the next day that, but

79

Smitty seemed to have decided upon his role, the dominant one, at least, and this gave him a pretty fixed and forceful manner. The dominant role he had adopted was the cynical, wisecracking, poolroom buffoon and his choice was very effective because he looked the part exactly, he was small with a hatchet face and yellow, bad teeth. Henry was a puffing, always winded fat boy, he didn't do much except laugh at appropriate moments and repeat the last phrase of what someone said. Earle was tall and muscular and I guess he probably grew into what is known as a good-natured giant. He was seven months younger than me and I called him "Kid," but I wasn't being smart, seven months seemed like seven years; I called him kid with complete sincerity and without any ulterior motives.

Smitty and Earle were always having it out; however it wasn't unpleasant because Earle was genial and Smitty didn't take himself too seriously. Many people who have decided upon a dominant role feel called upon to defend it totally, but if Smitty lost a point he didn't take it as a personal affront and a rejection of all that is sacred and logical. He and Earle kidded each other all the time and each tried to get Henry and me to take their side. That night of my first hike after we had turned in they talked back and forth. They talked about the scoutmaster, and basketball, the various ways to cook meat and which way was best. Back and forth and the conversation took on a rhythm like a song. Smitty had a cigarette which he took out and lit up, cupping the flame from view so the scoutmaster, or an enemy sniper wouldn't spot him. He passed it around, but I declined saying I had a sore throat. The tempo of the conversation faltered as they took drags then the beat picked up again, they agreed and disagreed and challenged each other, talking about airplane identification, what they would do to the enemy if they were on the battlefield, war atrocities—Smitty and Earle carried the melody and Henry was the chorus, laughing in the breaks, or repeating a phrase.

The Japs always rape women, Earle said. I know they do, little girls too, Smitty agreed. Yeh, even little girls Henry said. The Germans cut off your dick, Smitty said. Earle didn't believe him. Sure they do. Henry laughed. Do they, really, Earle said. Sure to prisoners in the concentration camps, Smitty assured him. They wouldn't do it to me, Earle said, they better not try it with me. Me either, Henry said. You don't use it Smitty said to Earle. Earle asked Smitty what he meant. Smitty said he knew what he meant. Ha ha. I need mine more than you need yours, Earle said, goddammit. Bullshit, Smitty said and he said he didn't believe Earle could even jack-off. No, Earle, you can't even jack-off, Henry said. Earle said he could. Smitty said he couldn't. I can. You can't. Ha ha. Bullshit. I'm from Missouri, Smitty said, you gotta show me. Why should I show you, Earle said. Why should he, Henry said. Smitty dared Earle again. O.K., Earle said. Earle unzipped his sleeping bag. Henry took his flashlight from his sleeping bag and cupping the beam so it wouldn't shine to the sides put it on Earle. Hey look, Earle's got a hard on, Smitty said. Earle masturbated some and stopped. Smitty said that was nothing. Let's see you, Earle said. Smitty refused. Hey, Ed, Smitty called to me. Henry turned the flashlight on me. I pretended I was asleep. He's asleep. Are you chicken, Smitty, Earle asked. No, but you didn't even finish. You're chicken, Earle said. Yeh, Henry said, chicken. Smitty unzipped his bag and Henry put the beam on him. Smitty took his out and

81

did the whole thing. Smitty dared Earle to finish. Earle said he bet Henry wouldn't. Henry said he would too. Henry held the light on himself and did it. Put it over here, Earle said. Henry turned the light on Earle and he finished then Henry shut the light off.

For a while everything was quiet except for the forest sounds, then they talked a little more and gradually stopped. When I was sure everyone was asleep I scooted down in my sleeping bag and tried it some, but nothing happened and I felt foolish.

That hike was the first time I had ever spent a night away from my parents and when I got home the next day I was treated like a returning hero.

A few weeks after the hike I was upstairs in my room getting ready for bed. I had on my pajama jacket and I was sitting on the side of the bed putting on my bottoms. I had one trouser leg on and I was pulling the other one on when I noticed myself and decided to try again.

For a moment, like the first time, nothing happened, then suddenly it came alive and I couldn't let go. The boys on the wallpaper all around the room, rolling hoops down the streets and wearing Silas Marner knickers seemed to jump off the cobblestones. It felt so good and I felt so alive . . . the dresser looked a richer brown and I was aware of the texture of my pajamas and I could smell the newly laundered sheets. I couldn't stop. There I sat on the side of the bed beating my meat like mad, with the door open and everything. Masturbation became an unbreakable habit with me. I developed the fixation that I itched, "just one little scratch," I would say, but that was only the overture I used to fool myself. One little scratch would lead to another, until finally I would drop all pretence and abandon myself to my hands. I was very unhappy but it was a good unhappiness. Physically it was wonderful, yet it was more than that. The physical pleasure was like the scouts, I mean it was outside, but the unhappiness was deep inside me. I always wore a sad expression and had gigantic inner struggles with myself to break the habit, but the inner struggles added zest, made life seem monumental. Once I succeeded in breaking the habit, peace was dull, I let myself backslide into the old fixation and struggles and I had something to do again. I suppose I nursed my habit through adolescence much as an unattractive person magnifies and recalls over and over again a measly love affair.

8

I SAID OVERNIGHT HIKES were the favorite activity—
they were if you exclude summer camp, or better yet,
consider summer camp as a gigantic overnight hike,
which is exactly what it was. Summer camp was talked
about the entire year and the boys who had been
seemed to the rest of us to have a mystic aura of scouting lore surrounding them: they lead the song festivals
and always talked among themselves about the way we
did this, or when we did that at summer camp. I joined
the scouts in the late fall and by the time summer camp
rolled around the following year I was willing to do
anything for two weeks at Camp Falksmith. My mother
thought that I should wait another year, but my father
said I had worked hard and I deserved it. Finally I was
allowed to go. Mother went with me when the tuition

was paid and gave the scoutmaster a long lecture on the care and treatment of her son, but a number of other mothers did the same thing so I did not feel too badly. Finally the big day arrived and boys from all the troops in the vicinity assembled at the rendezvous point. Big school buses that had been chartered for the trip stood dull and flat and ominous in the early morning fog waiting for us. Just before we left the sun began to break through—everything lost the cutout look and took on three dimensional qualities and the buses turned bright yellow and began to glisten.

Summer camp was an overnight hike carried to its perfect, its logical conclusion. Outside of the two weeks at Camp Falksmith I never experienced in reality anything carried to its logical conclusion that was right. Camp Falksmith was perfect. The time didn't seem to fly, it didn't seem to go slowly either—it was suspended in a delicious void. Homesickness was the only part of the encampment that could have been negative and instead it was turned into an advantage. After a night or two at camp a little homesick gnawing of wanting to see your folks and to do things around the house started, gradually the gnawing grew stronger and stronger and just before homesickness tipped the balance of enjoyment, making each day a liability instead of an asset the two weeks were up. The closing days of the encampment we all grew very nostalgic for Camp Falksmith, the friends we'd made, the good times we'd had, the songs sung.

At summer camp we would get up in the morning to a bugle, grab our toilet kits and go down to the wash area designated to the lower east hill cabins, which was our cabin group. We scrubbed up at long, urinal looking, troughs; after we finished washing up we went back

86

to our cabins to dress; halfway through dressing the bugle would blow for breakfast, the table leader for the day would yell for us to hurry up and we would pile out and line up in front of the cabin. Our table leader would form us up with the men from the other cabins in our group and we would march down to the chow hall. In front of the chow hall we would assemble with the other cabin groups into one big formation and wait for the doors to open for breakfast. While we waited we sang songs led by the camp songmaster and if chow was late we sang "Here We Sit Like Birds in the Wilderness" very loudly. When the chow hall opened we would file inside, line up at the tables, stand at attention, bow our heads, say a scout prayer and then sit down and eat. When breakfast was over we went back and cleaned up our areas. After that we started on the activity roster and the day began in earnest. We learned handicraft, we went swimming, canoeing, we played a game where you wrestled and captured each other's men, we went hiking in the woods which were silent, deep, green, mysteriously secret sweet, godlike and Indianlike, we had contests and races and worked on our advancement and in between we ate two more meals. On Sundays we had church in an open air chapel and at night there were council fires deep in tradition and wisdom. Once each encampment we could go to town. My first encampment we went to town, saw a movie and stopped by a soda fountain for cokes. The soda fountain had a jukebox in the corner and when we came in "Sentimental Journey" was playing, which seemed perfect—very far away from homish and soldier-like. Except, however, for the one night we were allowed to go into town the days ended with a council fire. After the council fire we would pick the way back to our cabins through the darkness, not looking at objects directly, using our night vision, the way we had been taught, the stars twinkled high overhead and occasionally someone would yell, or laugh. When we got to the cabins we would climb into the bunks and our mood would change. We would tell dirty jokes and exchange stories about sex with each other for hours. None of us were blasé about sex, so we did not go for subtlety and every statement was bulging with description: dripping, slushy, stark naked, titty pink, gaping, big as a bull, heaving, wild-for-it, long thick hairs— sometimes, when we ran out of sex talk, we would lie quietly and listen to the boys in the cabin next to ours on the right hand side who never ever seemed to run low on stories and all of whom interrupted one another and shouted very loudly trying to get in their variation first.

Needless to say I learned a lot and picked up skills right and left, I also underwent a number of changes at summer camp; some changes were abrupt about faces, other changes evolved so gradually they went unnoticed and were imperceptible unless viewed over a long span of time, of course the long range changes weren't accomplished in the two weeks at Camp Falksmith, rather, in those cases, summer camp was just the place where the seed was planted, or the first tiny crack in the dike of this, or that outlook began to appear.

Once when I had a job driving two-man streetcars I worked with a Negro conductor who was very belligerent. He would snatch fares and give short answers and if an automobile was loitering on the tracks in front of us he would hop off the streetcar, run around up to the driver of the automobile and give him a piece of his mind, then he would run back to the streetcar, I would open the door and he would hop aboard and stand up in the front of the streetcar with me and tell me about that stupid white sonofabitch. Of course, discourtesy wasn't a characteristic peculiar to just my conductor; but he wasn't a grumpy, or evil guy who you would expect to be discourteous, I mean, his belligerency wasn't just plain irritability, or troubles at home, or something. He was rude with a vengeance. I watched him day after day going along being a shit, not calling out the streets, herding the people with unnecessary roughness to the rear, giving me the signal to pull off just as someone reached for the door. One day a passenger called him Boy and we had a big crisis. The conductor started shouting and the passenger started shouting—the conductor was going to call the inspector and have him thrown off, the passenger was going to get him fired and they kept going at it back and forth.

Perhaps I should have spoken to him, given him a long lecture on tolerance, but I am very cautious about giving out wisdom. A lot of people think of wisdom as a ladder, or steps that you climb getting wiser and wiser with absolutesmartness at the top and a favorite game they play is guessing who is higher upon the various ladders—such and such is more mature (higher upon the ladder) when it comes to that, but I am wiser when it comes to this, etc. . . . I don't know—I think of wisdom more as a circle, like a bull ring and how absolute-smartness, which is in the middle of the circle, looks depends upon your position in the ring: how close you are to the middle, whether you happen to be on the sunny, or shady side, etc. It is very difficult to say whose position in the ring is more correct, in fact, in my case, I am always shifting around and my position keeps changing. Take for an example my relationship with people, some days I think it is the ultimate, the last word in wisdom, dead in the center of the ring, so to speak, to be kind and help one's neighbor, to sit by the side of the road and be a friend to man and sometimes I think the closest thing to absolutesmartness is for everyone to kiss my ass. Besides in the case of the passenger calling the conductor Boy I couldn't say he didn't mean anything. It is very difficult to be sure of what he meant. He may have meant Boy, Fellow, Mac, or he may have meant boy, uncle, sambo, nigger. I can't say the conductor didn't have grounds for his militancy, just as there are grounds for many things.

But, anyway, my conductor didn't particularly stand out, he had a lot of company. I knew a lot of discourteous conductors, also I knew a lot of racially belligerent Negroes and White people—as a matter of fact, racial belligerency is an environmental hazard of living in the U.S.A. Racial belligerency is roughly equivalent to the belligerency between the sexes, just as you don't seem to suddenly grow up in your relationship toward the opposite sex (instead you must work your hate out by devious dirty tricks such as bragging, standing dates up, being late, being unfaithful) you don't suddenly seem to grow up in your relationship toward another race either—belligerency doesn't fall away all at once the way you take off a damp swimming suit. I think I began to squirm out of my swimming suit of hate, dulled my militancy, irrational militancy, that is, first had a crack in the dike of my belligerency, irrational belligerency, that is, at summer camp on the cartilage of Peterson's nose.

The chow hall at summer camp was a rectangular, squat building and it looked to me like King Arthur's feast hall, or the main compound building in a concentration camp. Depending upon my mood I entered the chow hall with my hand stuck in my belt holding an imaginary sword, or with my eyes squinted, humming "The Star-Spangled Banner," determined to give nothing but my name, rank and serial number, but inside instead of animal skins or torture equipment the chow hall was furnished with picnic tables and long benches. At the head of each table was a kitchen chair where the table leader sat. The job of the table leader was to keep order and to pass out the first serving which was placed on the table family style. Seconds and thirds were served cafeteria style at the back of the chow hall from the cook's window. Practically everyone got at least seconds. When the line for seconds got pretty long the cook who was watching us from his observation slot would unhook the latch on the wooden flap that sealed his serving window, swing the flap outward like an upside down drawbridge, lock it in the open position and start refilling our plates. Sometimes at the evening meal halfway through the line for seconds, or thirds, the cook would abruptly stop serving and announce, "Kitchen is closed!" Then he would reach up for the latch as if he were going to close the serving window.

"But why, Cookie?" we would shout.

The cook would pause with his hand on the latch and pretending impatience say very loudly, "I'm going to town to get some entertainment!"

"But, Cookie, you don't have to do that!" we would yell back.

"No, I don't?" the cook would ask, "Why not?"

"We have a great entertainer here."

"You do?" he would say.

"Sure we do," we would assure him.

"Who?" he would challenge us.

"You know who."

"No, I don't, who?"

"Mr. Pumpkin Stew," someone called (then we would shout the name of the next boy to be served, the boy nearest the cook's window).

"Him?" the cook would ask, critically eyeing the first boy in line.

"Yes, HIM!" we shouted and the boy would have to give a performance of some sort.

"Well, O.K." the cook would agree and he would call his helpers and they bunched around the opening of the serving window leaning on the sill and watched.

Usually the boy would keep saying, I can't, and try to get out of it. If he took too long the cook would pretend he was disgusted and reach for the latch holding the flap again and act as if he were going to close the window.

"I guess you guys were kidding me," he'd say.

"No!" we would howl and then we would yell at the boy and threaten him until he finally did a number.

One day as I came to the window for seconds the cook said he was closing and reached for the latch so I had to entertain. I started out singing "The White Cliffs of Dover," but I couldn't remember the words, so I started over again with "Yankee Doodle" and while I sang I did a little imitation of the crippled guy that played the fife. Outwardly with the fife and all, probably I seemed like any of the other boys, but inside I was lost without a map, or compass.

I was the only Negro at Camp Falksmith, the other three guys in my troop were charity cases and didn't come and the other troops represented didn't have any Negroes at all. I was the only Negro and I was performing. I was in a turmoil—perhaps I didn't use exactly these words, but I was thinking: should I draw a line? . . . where's the line? . . . am I doing my number just as another scout? . . . am I betraying the colored race? There I was—even when part of me got carried away and started imitating the fifer in the spirit of seventy-six; there I was, searching for a footpath, a trail of correct behavior, lost in the junglelike confusion of my mind, armed with, or impeded by a thousand things: half truths, fear of humiliation, companionship, the pledge of allegiance, desire for esteem, traditions—in the meantime, the voices in me, who usually agreed with one another and in clear situations gave me tons of sage Thanatopsissounding advice, were lost too and to cover their confusion had started to argue heatedly, they defended and prosecuted me, rattling back and forth. Although their argument was just a smoke screen to cover up their inadequacy, I found myself, as is often the case, being affected completely by what they said and I listened to them as if my life depended on it. Dancing for white folks—happy coon, one voice accused. The other boys did it, why shouldn't he? another voice defended. It's different. It isn't. They're white. They're his buddies. They're white and they'll turn on him. They won't. They will—Uncle Tom. It was his turn, stupid. Uncle Tom, Sambo . . . White folks' nigger.

I finished and I got a big hand and the cook piled my plate up and I went back to my table.

At summer camp we all bragged and complained to one another about how busy we were kept, but suddenly after supper when we had an hour free time lay dead. We stood around in front of the chow hall shooting the bull and gesturing with our hands the way Army pilots did on Coca-Cola posters. Gradually we drifted

93

off, one by one back to our cabins to write postcards and by the time the bugle blew for council fire assembly the drill ground was clear. It was pretty far into the free hour the same day I did my number, most of the boys had drifted off, when a fellow I didn't know too well, a fellow named Peterson who lived in the cabin next to ours that knew all the sex stories, walked up to me.

"Wherefo youall learn to sing like dat chile," Peterson said, trying to imitate what was supposed to be Negro dialect.

A voice inside me said, I told you so, I told you so.

"Leave me alone," I said.

"Why whatfo is de matter wid youse boy . . . ain't you friendly?" he said. He put his hand on my head and rubbed it.

Maybe he was only trying to be friendly, just joking with me the way we all kidded one boy who got so nervous when he had to sing that he had to start over three times. Maybe he's just kidding, a voice tried to soothe me—suddenly I hated the sonofabitch.

I slapped his hand down.

"Boy whatfo is de matter wid youall?" he said.

I told him if he came in the woods with me I would show him what the matter was and I started walking toward the trees. He and all the guys who had been standing around followed me. I walked along in the woods until I came to a clearing that had been formed when the wind blew a dead tree over. The trunk had shattered in several parts when it fell and the pieces were pushed back from the stump forming a crude circle.

I turned around. Peterson's expression said, come on now, let's tell them we were only kidding . . . ha ha . . .

94

that'll be a good joke on them won't it . . . ha . . . ha.

I stood there.

"Boy what's de matter?" Peterson said.

BLIP—I hit him one in the face. The other boys had circled around us. "Take it back," I thought I said aloud, but I must have said it to myself. I hit him some more. Peterson swung at me halfheartedly and grazed my shoulder. BLIP—I hit another good one in the face. Suddenly he stepped back and put down his dukes.

"I'm not going to fight you," he said. "You've probably got a razor."

"I don't have any old razor," I said. "You're chicken!"

He didn't move, I think he really thought I had a razor.

We looked at each other. I spat on him, I misjudged the distance and it landed just below his lips and bobbed up and down from his chin before he wiped it off. He began to whimper and suck in his breath. He backed away from me. He was crying and his shoulders were going up and down and he kept calling me sonofabitch. Finally he got his courage together. He stopped backing up and charged me and I had the most perfect physical moment I had ever known.

Once I saw this movie about a guy trapped in Japanese territory. Just as he is ready to escape and when time is very important he is cornered in a warehouse by a Japanese Admiral who is a judo expert and they fight a duel among the crates and things. Finally the admiral charges and the American, who knows judo too, flips him with a fancy twist and escapes. When Peterson charged me I tried to flip him the way I had seen it done in the movies, I had tried it before and I have tried it since and it never worked, but that time it worked perfectly. Peterson arced in the air and crashed against the stump of the tree in the middle of the ring. I jumped on him and smashed him in the nose. He tried to shield his face, but I smashed him a couple more before the other guys broke it up.

The next day as I was fixing my bunk one of my cabinmates came in and told me Peterson was outside and that he wanted to apologize. I climbed into my bunk and casually folded my hands under my head. I knew I could beat him. I snorted and I told my cabinmate to tell Peterson to come in, but he didn't want to come in so I went to the door, I put a hand on each side of the doorsill and scowled at him.

"What do you want, Pimpleface," I said.

He started to explain, but I interrupted him.

"I bet you got all those pimples from jacking-off," I said.

He tried to start again, but I interrupted him again.

"I bet you came around here to apologize so I won't kick your ass anymore," I said.

He stood there.

I spraddled my legs and crossed my arms over my chest the way captains of pirate ships did.

"You'd better get out of here fast, you pimpled faced landlubber before I kick your ass some more," I said and he left.

The night before we went home from summer camp I had a bad dream. I dreamed that all of my buddies turned on me and wanted to feel my hair. I began to run through the woods, but they chased me. I climbed up a tree, but someone saw me and they chopped the tree down. Just before the tree came crashing to the ground I began to beg for mercy. Spare me I shouted down to them, spare me . . . I thought you were my buddies.

We are, they shouted back, we only want to feel your hair, we have a new boy who wants to feel your hair. You can't, I said and I begged them not to. They chopped the tree down anyway and when I hit the ground they surrounded me and everyone took turns feeling my hair, but it didn't hurt like I seemed to feel it would. . . . Finally I passed into a sounder sleep.

The last morning we got up to the bugle as usual, washed up and marched down to breakfast. I had decided to make up with Peterson and all through the meal I kept looking around for him, but I didn't see him. After the meal the head counselor stood up. We all called him Pinky. Pinky looked like a jolly monk and he joked a lot too in a YMCAish sort of way, and he was very man to man with us, but tender too and I guess you could say condescending, if a grownup can be condescending to a child.

"Boys," he said and held up his hands for silence. Gradually the room became quiet except for the rasp-rasp of a branch that needed pruning brushing against the screen of one of the chow hall windows and occasionally someone would fidget and knock a utensil off the table and it would hit the floor with a clatter.

"Boys, I want to speak to you of a serious matter. Last night after the big council fire I decided to walk awhile under the beautiful stars—which I did . . . coming home again, as I walked past one of the cabins on the hill, I heard some of the vilest type of talk it has ever been my misfortune to hear. . . . Sex talk fitting only for the lowest waterfront hangout, inhabited by thieves and cutthroats . . ."

I watched Pinky waiting for our cue to laugh—we all

97

did that every evening, we all talked like that as soon as we got to our cabins—I was sure he was kidding. But with a straight face he went on to tell us how hurt and shocked he was—we all do that, we all do the same thing, didn't he know that. When I realized Pinky wasn't playing a joke I was frightened. At that time I hadn't run into the little slogan that goes more or less, "We know what we want to know."

". . . I am sure you boys are as shocked as I was," Pinky was saying, ". . . and I am as sure you chaps feel as I felt that each boy in that cabin was a disgrace to the scouting spirit and Camp Falksmith," we all nodded, Pinky went on to say that the boys had been ordered to pack their equipment and had been driven home by the camp medic so as not to contaminate the rest of us, we all nodded. Pinky read out the names of the boys that had been expelled and Peterson was one of them, so I never got a chance to make up with him. Then Pinky handed out the awards and I got a medal for placing second in firebuilding.

There was a ritual to leaving Camp Falksmith. After all the awards were handed out we went to our cabins and packed our gear. When we were all packed we marched down the hill assembled in front of the mess hall and sang the traditional farewell song to Camp Falksmith. Then we were each given a sandwich and an orange to take with us. Cookie would take time out from the big welcome-to-Camp-Falksmith-dinner he was fixing and come out and wave good-bye to us. We filed up on the trail leading out of camp. Trees lined each side of the trail and formed an arch over us and there was a wonderful smell there that I loved. I can't remember what the odor was like, yet whenever I think of the trail my nose twitches and I remember I loved it. Then with the air of troops moving up to new positions we marched down to the highway where the big yellow buses were waiting. We would get into the buses and go home, someone always starting singing "A Hundred Bottles of Beer on the Wall" and whenever we got to a town without planning among ourselves, just like it was automatic or something, we all sang louder and waved from the windows.

9

IF I PRETEND MY LIFE IS HISTORY I would call the time roughly covering high school, the time during the Big Freeze, my dark ages. Better yet, the time of the Big Freeze was a war, or even more closely the aftermath of an old imperialistic war, when everything is more, or less settled down except for an occasional uprising. We, the kids in my group within a year or so of my age, represented the colony and our moms represented the mother country. Each mother was a political party unto herself and during peace they were always watching and trying to outdo one another and being very careful about party pride. Humph, Mother would say when she hung the phone up after talking to one of her friends who she felt was in the red—Mother kept a sort of running list on who she owed visits to and who owed them to her—does she think I am supposed to visit her all the time. . . . I was over there twice and she hasn't set foot in my door for almost a month. No child, Mom would go on, nodding and reassuring herself, I never ran after anyone and I'm too old to start. . . . She asked me over, humph . . . I told her I was sorry, I just had to get my ironing done. However when Mom and her friends felt we were revolting they closed their ranks solidly against us and issued unanimous decrees of conduct and we were quickly put down. We never even realized that we were uprising or being suppressed. We were always urged forward and being told about taking our place as growing young men and young ladies and quite innocently every now and then we would reach to put a finger on the reins of government; however, sometimes we had an inkling we were straying from the proper path.

One summer Mom asked me why I was talking on the phone so much and I told her I was getting the arrangements straight. Arrangements straight for what, she wanted to know. I wasn't able to lie. Well, I said, the gang decided instead of all going to the movies one Sunday we would go to Riverview instead. Do you mean, she wanted to know, to Riverview, the Amusement Park. Yes, Mam, I said. Do you mean, young man, all the way to Riverview, the amusement park in Chicago. Yes, Mam, I said. She asked me if such and such's mother knew about it, or did such and such's mother. I said I didn't know. Mother got on the phone and made some calls to her friends and the decree came down that we couldn't go.

The most suspicious mothers in the world live in the Chicago suburbs, at least the most suspicious mothers in the world lived in the Chicago suburbs in my group,

group one. The suburbs of Chicago are made up of medium and small towns and the people in each town were divided into four groups, anyhow that's how Mom and her friends felt we were divided: first, there was the Negro Group, group one, the group to which I and my gang belonged along with our folks, then there was the Black Trash Group, the White Group and the White Trash Group. When our plot to go to Riverview was discovered our mothers grilled and questioned us. Well, young man, Mom said to me . . . You think you're grown now . . . quite the young man, wet on a post and smelled it, humph . . . we take you children to River-view every summer, don't we . . . just what time did you young men and ladies plan to come home. Finally, just when our mothers were cooling down, it came out that there would have been an equal number of boys and girls and that we had planned to pair off. Our mothers hit the ceiling again.

Our mothers had two aims that obsessed them. The first was that we should be children while we were children and the second was that we should be more, or less, sexless. The second aim was really only a facet of the first, the don't try to be grown too fast one, but it was emphasized to such a proportion it became an obsession in its own right. The amusement park plot completely violated both aims, so our mothers really clamped down on us and war, or better, a state of emergency was declared and we were placed under martial law. We expected them to cool off and for the martial law to end, at least, by the time summer was over; instead, it continued on and on, we didn't realize it at the time but the Big Freeze had begun.

I suppose the Big Freeze was inevitable and only a matter of time. I guess our graduation from grade and preparation for high school meant to our mothers we were approaching a dangerous age and if the Riverview plot hadn't been discovered that summer we would probably have been put under martial law in the fall when school started. My freshman year, the Big Freeze was mild; however at the beginning of the fall term of my second year it was discovered that two of my classmates were pregnant and when our mothers heard of it the Big Freeze lost its mildness. One of the girls was even from our group, or I thought she was until my mother explained to me that the girl had only been invited to our parties because she seemed too nice for the Black Trash, but by no stretch of the imagination could she be called in our group. . . . No, child, humph, no stretch of the imagination, just rif-raf. Anyway, after that, for the next two years, the Big Freeze was really on, but during my senior year it became mild once again. In the middle of summer vacation between my junior and senior years one of the boys in our group ran away and he wasn't caught and brought home for two weeks. He stayed home the rest of the summer, but right after school he ran away again and joined the army. It was said the boy's father drank heavily and that he was very mean when he did, the boy was condemned a lot too for being prodigal; notwithstanding our mothers eased up the martial law and the Big Freeze petered out.

The first year, as I said, the Big Freeze was lenient, it consisted simply in our mothers not granting us the new privileges that generally go along with a promotion to high school; we grumbled a little at the beginning, until our mothers explained to us that we were good, special children, and they weren't just turned loose to run wild like common trash. However, as I said, just after the beginning of my sophomore year, when the news of the pregnancies got out, all leniency was dropped: we couldn't walk along with a girl, or we couldn't be out after dark if there were girls in the group, and we had to be very careful about not acting too grown and things. The big change, however, was in the girls themselves. Before the second year of the Big Freeze the girls in the group were in league with the boys, at a party when you danced with your special old lady she would even let you hold her rear, but suddenly the girls changed over and started siding with our mothers against us. The fundamental consequences of the girls going against us was that the emphasis of parties, parties were our number one social recreation, was switched. Before the emphasis of a party was on sex, but after the girls turned against us the emphasis was switched, or more correctly waylaid, from sex to gang fights and wine drinking. Actually, if I am honest, I guess I must admit there weren't really any gang fights; not in our group anyway, the Black Trash group had one, we never did though, but we were always talking and planning strategy for the big battle we were going to have with the Negro group from the town next to ours. Every now and then when the party got dull we'd grab one another and pretend to work each other over and practice what we were going to do to the other guys the day of the big battle. Actually, too, there wasn't much wine drinking. Sometimes though, one of the guys would sneak a small bottle into a party and we would chip in on it and pass it around smacking our lips each time we had a turn. Then a guy would act high and put his hands on a girl's breast, or legs. If the girl got real mad and said she was going to tell we would all beg her not to, saying the guy would get into a lot of trouble and that he was just high and didn't know what he was doing.

After the Big Freeze came whenever girls from Chicago happened to be at one of the parties everyone tried for them. Girls from Chicago were like the girls in our group were before the Big Freeze, maybe there wasn't a Big Freeze in Chicago, or maybe it was because they were away from home or something. They'd dance close and they would let you rub them and they were always snapped right up as partners. I never got one as my old lady for the evening during the Big Freeze because except for that one time at Sarah's party when I was King of the Ball, so to speak, I didn't carry enough weight, I wasn't important enough, to move some of the other guys out who would try for them.

Out of all the parties Sarah's is the one I like to remember best. It was way back, just at the fringe of the Big Freeze, just before it started and it was a great triumph for me. In fact, through a chain of events, Sarah's party caused the Big Freeze to come sooner than it would have. Of course, the Riverview affair definitely hastened the Big Freeze and being the hit of the evening at Sarah's party, anxious to relive my glory, I was the main instigator of the Riverview plot—I could just see Yvonne and myself, Yvonne shared my triumphs at Sarah's party, in the tunnel of love.

Sarah's party was sort of a late graduation party. Originally it was going to be held the Friday night we graduated from the eighth grade, but the PTA decided to give a social that night for the graduating class and their parents, so the party was postponed for two weeks.

Sarah's party was held on the lawn in her backyard. At the same time the grownups had a get together inside the house. Sarah's party was perfect. The weather was

106

fine, everything. There was even, through some miracle, an exactly equal number of boys and girls. Since our parties consisted mainly of dancing it was important to have close to the same number of boys and girls; however we were told we had plenty of time for that sort of thing and a party list was drawn up simply on the grounds of what nice children were available. Anyway the law of averages caught up with us at Sarah's party and there was someone for everyone.

All day the weather was clear, but I watched the sky distrustfully. I kept saying to myself, it's going to rain, sure it's going to rain, the day dragged and dragged then suddenly it was time and I had to hurry and take my bath and get ready. My dad was working and I had to wait for my mother to get ready so I could walk her over. While I waited for my mother and on the way over to the party I was very preoccupied, busily trying to think up cool things to do. We had only one goal and that was to be cool. We wanted to be cool in everything we did, in our walk, in our talk, in our games and most of all we wanted to be suave, blasé—cool, cool, lovers.

When we got to the party Mom went up the front steps into the house and I walked around the side, following the music until I came to the backyard. There was the party. Everyone was all dolled up, the kids who were already in high school, or, who hadn't graduated yet wore suits and party dresses and all the graduates wore their commencement clothes: we wore white pants, white shirts, white shoes, blue coats and blue bow ties and the girls wore white dresses and shoes. A tall hedge surrounded the backyard on three sides, Chinese lanterns were hanging, carefully spaced, in a big X across the yard, a card table had been brought out and set up and a phonograph, hooked up to an extension cord and some records had been put on the table, Sarah's father was making a barbecue pit and a plank with a white tablecloth draped over it, had been placed on the bricks to hold the sandwiches and punch.

I met Yvonne that night, the first girl of my dreams. She was visiting her cousin, a girl in our group, for the summer. When I met her that night I thought she was the finest thing I had ever seen. She had a pink dress, two long braids and big eyes that reminded me of a song called "Ramona" that Mom would sing around the house sometimes in the evening around sunset. When the punch was served, which signaled the beginning of the party, another fellow named George Evers and myself both tried for her.

Our parties had four regular sections, or movements: first there was the overture when people arrived and got settled. Then when the punch was served, or the pop opened the second section began. The second section was the scramble for a partner and there was quite an art to it. You had to juggle the facts between the partner you wanted and the partner you could get and there were a lot of variables to take into account: how much prestige your partner would give you, how close she would dance, how much necking she would do, how stiff the competition was and how much you had to offer. Human nature being what it is the scramble usually began with us rushing the two, or three belles and each one of us putting in our bid. Then things began to level off and we sifted down the scale according to our luck and to what they thought of us to the plainer girls. Very early I saw the wisdom of acquiring a weird taste, which I did and in that way I avoided the mainstream of competition. After the scramble which took place in the space of three or four records the third movement which consisted of socializing and dancing around began. Toward the end of the party the last movement would start, we each drifted back to our special partner for the evening to try and make out a little and maybe walk her home.

When the scramble started George Evers and I both made for Yvonne, but he was a grade behind me and so he didn't stand much of a chance and I won her for my old lady for the evening. I liked her and after the socializing started I cooled it back and danced with her whenever I could make it appear accidental.

Our favorite records were all slow. Before the Big Freeze the girls would stand very, very close. The music would work easy and steady and we would do a dance we called the slow drag, grinding and pushing against each other with every thump of the music—dum dum dum dum dum dum dum dum dum

> *I'm going up on the mountain* (*pause*)
> *To face the rising sun* (*pause*)
> *If I find anything good*
> *I'll bring my good man some*

we would clutch, and sweat, and hug and all the gang would break in on the chorus with the record

> *He used to be yours* (*pause*)
> *But he won't be yours* (*pause*)
> *Anymore*
> *Anymore*
> *An ny mor or ore*

Our mothers, and the fathers with daughters, didn't like

to see us slow drag and whenever some grownups looked in on us to see how we were getting along we would play fast records and jitterbug for them. They would laugh and talk about how fast children were getting and call us mannish little devils. In about the middle of the party at Sarah's all the grownups came out in a big bunch to watch us. I was dancing with Yvonne at the time, someone put on a fast record and we started jitterbugging.

When I spun Yvonne away from me she did a funny little hop that I had never seen before. The next time I threw her out I tried to do the hop myself. It came out a little differently, but somebody noticed me and said, "Look at Edward." Then Yvonne started imitating my imitation and the grownups began to applaud and encourage us, look at those little things go.

The record ended and they put some more fast ones on. Yvonne and I kept it up and the other children stopped dancing and started watching us too. I tried something else and I almost fell, but I caught myself and it looked as if I had planned it that way. They started clapping and saying GoBoy, GoBoy. A couple of times we kicked each other, but we kept right on going and I did my stumble on purpose some more, catching myself at the last minute and we brought down the house. When the grownups went back inside the house everyone wanted to know where I learned the new step and I went through it with Yvonne and taught it to them. We began playing slow records again and soon afterward the fourth movement started and I went back to Yvonne.

The very first time I put my hands on Yvonne's rear she let them stay. She told me she thought I was a wonderful dancer and that she was glad she was my partner. When she said that I was in heaven, the gang all dolled up dancing, the used paper plates piled on the buffet board and on the card table with the records and phonograph, the moon in the clear sky, the Chinese lanterns, everything, the whole suburbs, spun and focused, blurred and refocused. I begged and begged my mother to let me take Yvonne home and since Yvonne and her cousin lived right on the way to our house Mom finally consented. On the way home I put my arm around Yvonne and she took my hand and put it on her breasts which were budding and she let me squeeze the nipples. When we got to a real dark spot I put my hand further up her dress than I had ever done before, with the exception of the time one of Sammy's girls, for an instant, what seemed like an eternity ago, had flung the door open wide.

I was well on my way to becoming a cool lover and I had a lot of plans, but shortly after Sarah's party the Riverview plot was discovered and the state-of-emergency was declared and everything had to be postponed.

Finally at the very end of the summer when they were sure the revolt had been put down and that we had learned our lessons our mothers relented and decided that one Saturday they would take us to Riverview themselves. The news didn't make me very happy. Oh, I was glad to get to go to Riverview; however, I knew it meant the end of my dreams of gloriously organizing and leading the gang on an expedition of my own. In just the two weeks between the time I first got the idea for the amusement park trip and my mother discovering the plot I had made every step of the journey a thousand times in my fantasy. All summer long despite the state-of-emergency I cherished my dream and I hated to lose it—I had thought about leading the Riverview trip so much until it was a part of me, it seemed official and preordained and my destiny. My big consolation was at Riverview. I planned to pick up where I left off with Yvonne; however, instead, my career as a cool, cool lover was nipped.

The amusement park was a long way from where we lived in the suburbs and the trip to and from Riverview was a grueling two hours each way—actually the plot to go to Riverview one Sunday afternoon instead of the movies would have never worked and if it hadn't been discovered it would have ended up on the childhood junkheap marked EXUBERANT SCHEMES. To get to Riverview we had to ride three different vehicles. We would take a commuter train to Chicago, then we would take an L to the Northside where we would change to a streetcar that would take us to within a block of Riverview. The trip was so long, halfway to Riverview we would always get hungry. Our mothers would say they would see if they could find something to hold us and then each one would bring out special, elaborate sandwiches they had prepared and that they called little snacks, they would tell each other how they had just whipped them together and praise one another's cooking.

Finally the big Saturday arrived and our mothers packed their two-stage lunches and took us.

I felt like a dethroned king and I was determined to remain aloof, but halfway to Riverview, when it was snack time on the train and Mom brought out stage one of the lunch my stomach betrayed me. At first I only took half of a sandwich. My mother asked me did I want some more. I said I didn't. Then she asked me why didn't I ask Yvonne over to have a sandwich with me. I said I didn't want to, but I got up immediately and went over to where she was seated with her cousin and asked her over. We ate two sandwiches apiece and Mom broke a precedent and went into stage two of her lunch basket and gave us each a piece of chicken. Yvonne didn't go back to the seat with her cousin and we rode along pointing out interesting things to one another from the window.

Suddenly when we got off the streetcar, one of the favorite places in my daydream, and started walking down the block of long white fence to the entrance gate, everything swooped back and I was in my fantasy. We got off the streetcar. Each guy helped his date down. The last girl tripped on the step and missed her date's hand. She stumbled forward trying to regain her balance and stepped off the safety island. Just then a big truck came around the streetcar and bore down on her. I lunged off the safety island and knocked her out of the way just in time.

But then we were at the entrance gate and Mom not me was giving the orders. We each had our money, but our mothers said they were going to treat us to admission and for us to stand over by the ticket taker while they bought the stub. I felt as if I was being squeezed and blown up at the same time. My head hurt. I grabbed Yvonne's hand, I told the ticket taker our mothers would pay for us and he let us go by and we ran into the amusement park. We ran through the gloomy entrance arch and burst into the brilliant sunshine. We were there at Riverview. We were at Riverview. The instant you go through the arch the whole park is there; you see it, hear it, smell it—you just know it is there: cotton candy, hurdy gurdys, rides, roller coasters, sailors, soldiers, drive 'em cars, freaks, carousel music—it was all there for Yvonne and I. We paused a second and then ran to the left and the first ride we came to was the Dive Bomber.

Riverview is laid out roughly like a circle and when I had come before we always began at the right, by the roller coasters and worked our way around counter-clockwise, pausing midway at the picnic grounds area to eat the big second stage of the lunch. Then we continued on around until we reached the gate that we had started from; three fourths of the way around the circle it would begin to grow late and we would start to hurry skipping more and more things. By the time we reached the last few rides we weren't stopping at all—besides, Mom would always say when we got to the Dive Bomber, even if we did have time I wouldn't let you get on that thing . . . it's too dangerous for grownups, let alone children.

The cockpits of the Dive Bomber where the people sat looked like huge double-nosed artillery shells. One nose was unoccupied. Yvonne ran through the gate and got in. I bought the tickets climbed upon the platform and got in beside her. The attendant flipped a big leather strap across our laps and notched it on a metal hook that was under my seat. He put it in the last notch, but it was still a little loose. I heard the gang run up to the gate. The attendant said we had room for one more and he pointed behind me to where the gang must have been standing. No, I said. He slammed the canopy door shut, climbed down from the platform, pulled it away and signaled to the starter. The motor started to hum. Just then my mother must have arrived on the scene. Edward, she called. Luckily, I was in the section away from the gate and I didn't have to face her. Mother called again, Edward. The way she was saying my name was really short for, Edward come here this minute. Edward, Mother called. I was weakening. Edward, Mother called again. The shell began to sway.

The Dive Bomber is a cross between a pendulum and a daredevil kid on a playground swing. There is a tall, thick metal post with a cross bar at the top making it look like a huge T, from each side of the T hangs a metal arm and at the bottom of each arm is attached a double-nosed shell. The two rods swing back and forth like clock pendulums, but instead of a uniform tick tock in small strokes the arms, and consequently the shell with the riders, swing in larger and larger arcs, not fast, but with a slow deliberate, yet free motion, pausing at the furthest point of each swing, then reversing its direction, back and forth in higher and higher arcs until finally the shells reach the top dead center and stop, quivering with the people upside down hanging from the straps across their laps. Then the shells slip off center and begin to move, gradually working down again through smaller and smaller arcs to a stop.

We rushed gently backward and then we rushed gently forward. Yvonne and I smiled at each other. The sweeps grew larger. Yvonne was wearing a summer skirt and the force of the swing pulled it calmly up toward her stomach each time we swung forward and I could see a piece of her thigh. Now our swing backward flashed us out past the gate that held the spectators back and I thought I saw the folks. We rushed forward then back, then forward again. I didn't feel too safe and I was sorry I was on the side the door opened on. I'm scared, Yvonne said, hold me. O.K., I said— but I couldn't seem to let go of the safety holding bar. We started backward. I thought the bar was magnetized and I was going to tell her so, but the force of the swing

115

pulled my words out until I couldn't even recognize them. Each swing was larger. We swung back past the gate that held the spectators back, we reached the peak of that swing and I shot a quick glance at the ground far below. I saw the gang and my mother and her friends with their heads thrown back watching us. The shell trembled a moment and shot down and forward. Yvonne scooted down in the seat and spraddled her legs to brace herself. The leather strap came up across her stomach and her dress billowed all the way up to it and I could have touched anything of hers I wanted to. We approached the top of the forward swing. I could see over the wall—the street—car tracks, in the distance, the skyscrapers in the downtown smoke, a car leaving a filling station, then only the sky, the color blue of a robin's egg. Someone had been screaming for a long time in the other end of our shell. Yvonne started screaming. We swooped down and back and there was the amusement park again and over there the gang and my mother and her friends. I shut my eyes when we started forward again, I opened them on the other side looking at the sky. Yvonne had been a little sick and her dress was smattered with pieces of Mother's sandwich and chicken. The shell paused, there was a cross breeze from me to Yvonne and so I couldn't smell anything—everything was so gentle and peacefully fresh, like harp music. Then the car shivered and we started backward again and I shut my eyes and began to scream with Yvonne. Back and forth, I felt sick, finally I thought, we should almost be stopping and I opened my eyes, but we hadn't even reached the top dead center swing where the thing stands completely on its head.

10

IN HIGH SCHOOL THERE WAS A CLUB for every imaginable activity: athletic clubs, language clubs, scholastic clubs, honorary clubs, homemaking clubs and besides the ones sponsored by the school there were a group of student fad clubs, such as the woman-hater club that the football team started. Every Wednesday they wore dark glasses and refused to speak to girls and even tried to avoid answering the teacher if she were a woman. If a member of the club was caught talking to a girl he was popped with wet towels in the shower after football practice. There was a throat club. Anyone who had been poked in the Adam's apple was automatically in the club and according to the club's constitution was officially eligible to jab other people in the neck. The throat club grew fantastically fast. It was very painful to get a finger in the neck and soon everybody walked around the halls with their hands up to their throats to guard themselves. In my sophomore year they started having coke dances every Wednesday and Friday after school. A group got together and formed a jitterbug club they called the Hotcats. The Hotcats bought themselves light blue sweatshirts on which they painted their names and figures of people dancing and when hot numbers were played they gave jitterbugging exhibitions. We stood around watching them: the colored kids in a bunch near the cafeteria cash register, the couples in a circle around the dancers, the stag boys near the phonograph, or bandstand and the wallflowers shifting around the outside of the circle striking up conversations among themselves. No one ever danced during the exhibition, nothing, I suppose, is so empty, sad and defeating as trying to dance when a ring has collected around some couples and people going past to join the ring urge you to stop dancing and come and watch them instead. Each foreign language department sponsored a club which you were required to join when you took the language, so when I started to study Spanish I joined the Spanish club. I wanted to be an officer of some sort, but I was always just a member. Officers were chosen from among the students who showed outstanding proficiency in learning the language, which I didn't, or from kids who already knew Spanish and were taking the course for a snap. The only function that I can remember the club having was party planning. On Christmas we would break a papier-mâché container that was hung from the ceiling and we would sing "Silent Night" in Spanish and there would be refreshments and dancing. If there were enough Negroes in a club they danced among themselves. Otherwise they didn't dance and the teacher would suddenly become very interested in discussing some obscure verb, or else give you some out of the way job, such as refreshment man, which was the job the other Negro in the Spanish club had, or phonograph man, which was my job. I was discontented—not with being phonograph man, the duplicity of that situation didn't reach me at the time, it was something more indistinct, yet environmentally indigenous than being phonograph man, or not making the football team. Perhaps it is better to say I felt unfulfilled, rather than discontented—I don't know, life seemed so unepic. My senior year I joined the Hi-C club and became a soldier in the army of Christ and for awhile everything changed.

Hi-C stood for High Schools for Christ. I was introduced to the Hi-C club through the boy who was usually my partner in afternoon chemistry lab, a boy named Alfred. Chemistry lab was given in the morning and afternoons, I had a period free both times, but I would go to the afternoon lab because there was nothing much to do at home. In lab Alfred was very quiet and I had simply put him down in my mind that way; however, when I got to know him I discovered he had another side to his personality. When he was working for Christ, Alfred became a different person, sure, aggressive and fearless.

One day Alfred invited me to go to a meeting of his club with him and I accepted.

The meeting was held in the dramatics room, which also doubled as an annex for the auditorium, it was just about to begin when we arrived. There were about ten people in the first two rows and the rest of the room was empty. As we were seating ourselves a girl in the first row got up from her chair, turned around to face the group and began to pray in a quiet voice. After the girl finished praying she sat down. Then a movie screen and a projector were set up by a couple of the boys and we were shown a film.

The lights were shut off and the movie began, the film wasn't pure black and white, it was greenish black and greenish white instead. Three words, "The Rescue Worker," were flashed upon the screen, some music started, but the sound went out almost immediately and the two boys working the projector began searching for the trouble; however, in the meantime, the projector was left running and the film unfolded its story silently. A lady sat in a neat farmhouse kitchen holding a baby. Her husband stood behind the chair with his hand on her shoulder. They were both smiling down at the baby. The husband went to a shelf and got a bible and came back and knelt by his wife and read something from the bible. They bowed their heads in prayer, he kneeling at the chair and she with one arm holding the baby and the other resting on his shoulder. There were placards on the walls of the kitchen like my aunt used to have. Out of the corner of my eye I could see the dancing beam streaming from the projector. The dramatics room was on the main hall and students were still milling around outside from late classes and once in a while a wall locker would slam. There was a melancholy, thin light seeping in under the double doors and now and then, less and less all the time, someone clacked closely past the doors cutting a quick shadow through the light. The baby in the movie was a boy. He grew up. One day his father's car wouldn't start and he fiddled around and fixed it. He began to fix other things around the farm. Suddenly the sound came blasting back in, way too loudly ". . . decided to go to the city to study at a mechanics school." It was turned down to the correct volume. The young man went to the city with high hopes, but he fell into bad company and drifted down and down, finally he ended up on skid row a derelict. The voice telling the story said there were hundreds of just such cases each week. There were shots taken from a patrolling car, or truck showing skid row hoboes drunk, or asleep in doorways, alleys and on the sidewalk. There was one hope for these derelicts, the movie voice said and that hope was the rescue missions. The camera started way back on what was obviously a cardboard model of a skid row block and as it got closer it switched to the actual street. The camera trained its view on a building that looked like a store. The camera came nearer. You could hear people inside singing a song called, "Throw Out the Lifeline," very slowly.

> *Throw out the lifeline, throw out the lifeline,*
> *Someone is sinking today.*
> *Throw out the lifeline, throw out the lifeline. . . .*

The camera stopped at the sidewalk. From the sidewalk you could see that the building had been a store, but that it had been converted, and instead of a shingle advertising groceries, or hardware, a sign over the door, in big black letters, running the width of the building, read RESCUE MISSION. The show glass on either side of the door had been painted white and bits of threatening and inspirational scripture had been lettered on the paint. Young Bible students doing field work as rescue workers came out of the mission in squads of four and five. The camera followed a group. The group walked down a street. They came upon a tramp in a doorway and they sang gospel songs to him. The tramp got up and went to the mission with them supported by a young lady and young man. At the mission he was given coffee and doughnuts and started on his rehabilitation. The voice in the film told of the always desperate shortage of rescue workers. Everyone, the voice said, couldn't be a volunteer worker, but at least we could all live so that our lives were guideposts and inspirations to others who did not know Christ. The Lord needed soldiers to fight Satan on the battlefield of sin in every walk of life. The film said the life of a Christian was the hardest life in the world. A feeling of oneness, to be soldiers for Christ, pervaded the meeting and we huddled together like men in an assault boat landing on an enemy shore, all leaning forward toward the screen. The film ran out and the roll spun around a couple of more times, flap-flapping before one of the projector boys shut it off.

The hall was still, way off someone was whistling, a click and snap of a fire-safety door being opened echoed through the halls. The voice in the film had said Jesus needed soldiers in his army and I wanted to be one. Someone got up to turn on the lights, but Alfred called them back and they sat down.

"Let us pray," he said. I knew what I wanted to do. I wanted to fight for the Lord. No matter how rough, I wanted to be one of his soldiers.

After we prayed and the lights were turned on, Alfred, who it turned out was vice-president of the Hi-C, introduced me to the club. A couple more members had come in during the film and there were fifteen in all. I wanted to join the club immediately, but they wanted me to go home and think it over for a week and they made up a list of excerpts from the Bible that they suggested for me to read.

The next week when I came to the meeting I was asked to tell what had happened. I told how I had prayed, how the devil had tried to tempt me and how reading the excerpts from the Bible had given me strength to resist him. I got a couple of amens as I spoke and I joined the club. We all got down on our knees in a line and each person said a short prayer. One Hi-Cer thanked the Lord for the black boy who was giving his soul to Jesus, but outside of that one time the fact that I was colored was never mentioned. When the meeting was ending I was asked to say the closing prayer.

The Hi-C had a long list of activities they boycotted because they were considered sinful: smoking, drinking, dancing, gambling, and one day I learned, when I happened to mention a picture I had seen, movies were also on the list and being boycotted. I pointed out that we had seen a movie my very first meeting (I loved my Sunday afternoon movie). I was told the movie we had seen was made by a company specializing in church films. I said there were some good movies. Everyone agreed, but Hollywood and the majority of films were sinful. That was that, I stopped going to the movies and whenever I passed a theater I felt a shiver of pride.

There was a Hi-C club in each suburban high school and although the membership in each individual club was small, when a number of clubs would get together, as we often did, and have a combined outing there would be fifty, or sixty people. My mother liked the Hi-C and so whenever I asked to go on an outing she would tell me I was getting to be a big boy and let me go. We had a good time at the outings; in the fall we went on picnics and roller skating parties, in the spring there were bicycle hikes and in the winter we went tobogganing at a huge park on the southwest side of Chicago.

The gigantic toboggan slide stretched into the sky thirty feet higher than the mountain it was built on. We climbed the mountain and then the steps up to the top of the slide. At the top of the slide the groups of people way below toiling up the mountainside with toboggans were victorious ants returning from pillaging the remains of an old picnic. At the loading section, five or six of us would get on the toboggan. We all wore a lot of clothing, but when we arranged ourselves on the toboggan, for safety's sake, a boy, a girl, a boy, a girl and we put our legs around the person in front of us and hugged them and the person behind put their legs in your lap and hugged you, we all knew and didn't know what we were doing and we felt a common, warm, guilty, treacherous, conspiracy. Then when the toboggan in front was completely down the slide and stopped we would start. The last person would give a shove and we would inch forward and the front of the toboggan would hang over the edge of the slide. To the lead man on the toboggan it looked as if he were suspended in mid-air and the first time, even knowing the routine, it was frightening; the slide dropped off steeply and over the front of the toboggan, nothing could be seen except the end of the chute curving gently forward, far, far below, the preceding tobogganers untangling themselves, ants struggling over something and the refreshment lodge, a discarded shoe heel. The toboggan would slide forward, lose its balance, waver—at that moment when the toboggan wavered, we would all take a deep breath, shut our eyes and shout.

In that instant we were having fun—the golden fleece.

When I look back and try to remember exactly where I had fun, the anticipation and the recollection get all blurred and run together. I was always going to have fun or had just had it, but the piece of time, of life, that we sat clutching one another on the toboggan, feeling the front gradually sink forward, that was fun. The toboggan would lose its balance, waver and then the nose would come down with a slow thud onto the steep slide. We would spurt down the chute, the snow spraying past, faster, bouncing along, faster, the slide would begin to flatten out and we would start to slow down. Sometimes we would intentionally spill the toboggan and sometimes we would see how far we could glide. At the top of the slide another set of ants would perch on the edge and then start down. I never thought I could get enough tobogganing, but I haven't gone for a long time.

Hi-C rapidly grew to be the big thing in my life. Every day before school there was a morning meditation, on Wednesday there was the meeting, there were the occasional outings and every Saturday night there was a big Youth-for-God rally in Chicago near the Loop. Disregarding the outings, which had no regularity, the Saturday rallies were the high point of the week.

On Saturdays I worked in Chicago for my dad at his business, but he would let me off early so I could go to Youth-for-God meetings. I would spruce up, change clothes and catch a bus downtown to meet the four other Hi-Cers who would regularly attend the Saturday night rally. We would meet in front of Walgreens on State and Madison in the heart of the Loop.

I felt very grown; standing on the corner waiting for

them, I remember we always met at eight-twenty, the Loop would just be getting into its evening stride, movie marquees flashing, streetcars starting and stopping, rich people, poor people. If they got there before I did I would shout at them and they would turn around and wave at me and I would run the last half of the block with the tails of my topcoat hitting my legs and we would all shake hands and say praise the Lord.

Youth-for-God Inc., which ran the Saturday rally, was a booming concern, it also sponsored the Hi-C clubs and they were in the process at that time of forming a Youth-for-God Young Peoples Rescue Workers Auxiliary to help supplement the mission rescue workers who were desperately undermanned.

A half an hour before the service began people would start to gather at the auditorium: students of the local theological seminaries, workers for God of every age and description, missionaries, delegations from rival youth organizations, newly saved Christians (since the program was geared only to acquiring new souls, not to keeping the interest of those saved unless they started to backslide most run-of-the-mill Christians at the rally were new), Hi-Cers, camp counselors and a few mission reformed drunks, pale, threadbare, weak-kneed and blankly trying to accustom themselves to the strange world of soberness. Ten minutes before the rally would start everyone would be in their seats, facing the stage upon which sat the huge fifty-man Youth-for-God Band in blue and gold uniforms and in front of them the master of ceremonies, speakers, and guests of honor in a line of chairs.

When it was time to start, the master of ceremonies would get up from his chair and advance to the microphone, lower it and extend his hand into the air for silence. A quiet and a peace would settle over the auditorium. Then the M.C. would get down on one knee cover his face and begin to pray quietly into the mike.

"Oh, God, look down on the multitude gathered here tonight. You know our weakness and our need for your guiding strength." I would sit quietly with my head down, occasionally straightening up and taking a quick look around.

"Oh, Lord," he would continue. "Remember the sick and afflicted of this world. Please, remember the oppressed and hungry . . . many people do not have enough to eat tonight. I ask you to look down upon them in their misery. Little children without ever having known your word pass away . . . with their souls unsaved." I always felt sad and inadequate when he spoke of the underdog, but, finally, usually at the end of his prayer, he would get to my part.

". . . We thank thee for these young people who have come to worship you, God . . . we are thankful and rejoice that so early in life when their bodies pulsate with the energy of Christ and when there are so many things to be done that they come." Then he would continue as if presenting our case before a heavenly tribunal. "It is a hard life, the life of a Christian—Yes, Lord, they know that, but they want to take up the banner of Calvary and fight in your army.

"Lord, bless the Johnsons . . . this young couple, Ralph and Janie, just married and now preparing to carry your word out to the people of distant lands who do not know the glory of your teachings." He would point to the Johnsons, or to some other missionary couple sitting on the stage. The couple would smile.

Missionary work is one of the last of the utopian

professions, most of which went out with divine right of kings. Jesus is a very lenient boss demanding only that you try to spread his word. If you are willing to do that, successful, or not, you can't go wrong. The system is foolproof. I remember after Youth-for-God Inc., set up the auxiliary rescue workers our Hi-C club joined and in a small way I got a taste of missionary work. During the time I went to skid row we never had a bad night. We couldn't lose. If we found only docile willing drunks to take to the mission it was fine, the Lord was with us. If we ran across a stubborn derelict, that was fine too, it proved how hard the battle was and how powerful our foe, Satan, was and if a drunk cursed us we leaned eagerly into his words—see how hard we try, what trials we endure for you Jesus. Sometimes the papers carry a story where some far distant missionary has been killed by, say, Equatorial Indians. This isn't a flaw in the system—not at all, the system is foolproof—a death in the line of duty simply assures the other missionaries how hard their lot is and the murdered missionary becomes a saint, or near saint.

After all the guests and speakers had been introduced we would have a silent prayer for them and then the Youth-for-God Band would give us a piece. After the piece the guest speakers would talk to us. Each speaker always interjected jokes into his message and we laughed heartily at each one, feeling victorious, thinking to ourselves, see things don't have to be smutty, this is good clean fun, Jesus had a sense of humor. There was always a unique message. For instance, there was a man who had dogs that would act out a skit while he delivered a sermon on liquor, another time there was a husband and wife team that did magic tricks as they praised the Lord and there was an Eskimo family that

128

told of their conversion and sang gospel songs in three languages. After everyone did his number the Youth-for-God Band would give us another piece and then the membership drive for souls would start.

"Dear God," the M.C. would say, "if there is someone out there in need of you . . . some poor soul trying to fight the problems of life alone . . . maybe he is depressed, maybe he is worried, perhaps he cannot see any reason in life . . . it is for them we pray. Please bow your heads." We bowed our heads, shutting our eyes automatically.

"If there is anyone here," he would say, "who needs God, raise your hand. . . . Don't be ashamed, no one will see you, just God. Raise your hand so we can pray for you. If there is anyone here who needs His saving grace, raise your hand. . . . Raise your hand so we can pray for you. Don't miss the opportunity . . . don't keep putting it off, we never know when God may see fit to call us to him. Someday—ah, there are two hands . . . God bless you my children. Come before it is too late. Is there something lacking in your life? Let Jesus come into your soul. There's another hand upstairs . . . and one down front on the right and another in the front . . . there's one on the side." I couldn't hold out any longer and I put my hand in the air. "There is one in the back." (me)

I guess theoretically you are only supposed to put up your hand once, but every time I attended the Youth-for-God rally and he called for souls I put my hand up. My mother told me when I was little I would have joined church every Sunday if she would have let me. The minister would always say you had to be born again and talk about the spirit of Christ and when the choir sang "Let the Little Children Come Unto Me" I would always want to join the church. Sometimes Mother would let me. Walking down the long aisle up to where the minister stood waiting to shake my hand, with the choir singing, I felt sort of born again, but afterward it seemed to vanish. The next week when the preacher started talking about the wonderful happiness of redemption I was afraid I had missed the boat and I would want to join again. At Youth-for-God rallies it was almost exactly the same thing except I had begun to feel there was no boat for me and after going back to the consultation room the first rally I attended I just contented myself with raising my hand while all the heads were bowed.

After the M.C. felt that he had gotten all the possible hands raised he would continue.

"Now, Christians, God sees your hands and loves you for it, but you must stand before the world, you know . . . He needs soldiers in His army. Now, before I let the congregation raise their heads you can put your hands down if you want to (I would ease my hand down), if you aren't ready to declare yourselves O.K. and God blesses you just the same, but if you can, keep those hands up in the air . . . hold them high, let the world know of your joy in Jesus. The meeting will close right after the next hymn and all the new brothers and sisters are welcome to meet in the consultation room for a few minutes after the service. All right everyone raise your heads."

We would lift our heads and everyone whose hand was in the air would be praised and congratulated.

We would all rise and sing the closing hymn accompanied by the Youth-for-God Band. The closing hymn was usually a trick one where we made motions with our hands while we sang, each chorus we would drop more and more words until finally we would end up just making motions.

When the rescue workers auxiliary was formed our Hi-C club was one of the charter members. Two Fridays a month we would go down to skid row and do missionary work. There were five people in the group I worked in, Alfred, another fellow named Jerry, two girls and myself. The last time I went to skid row Jerry couldn't come and there were only the four of us.

We checked in at the mission and drank a cup of cocoa apiece. Then we went out to patrol the four blocks that our territory consisted of. We linked our arms in each others' and went down the street singing hymns and handing out tracts. We had almost patrolled our area once when we came upon a man sitting on the curb, with his feet in the gutter and rocking his head from side to side.

Alfred began to talk to the man, the man sat with his hands in his lap, smiling to himself and staring straight ahead, acting as if he wasn't aware of our presence. We sang a hymn.

"Go away, kids," he said.

Alfred tried to talk him into going to the mission with us. No answer. We sang a hymn. Still he didn't answer he just sat staring ahead with his head rocking slowly. Alfred tried again. I told Alfred I thought we should leave him alone; because I didn't think he was drunk. Alfred said, of course he was and started to lead us in another hymn. No answer. I said the man didn't talk like he was drunk. Well, Alfred said, he was drunk. He began again asking the man to come with us. Sir . . .

"Goddammit," the man said. He tried to get to his feet. He had to grab the lamp post to keep from falling. He took a swing at us and lost his balance and fell in the street. Once I saw that he was drunk I felt ashamed.

"Come to the mission, Sir," I said bending over the man, "I know what I'm asking you. Sir . . . I know it's hard to be a Christian . . . it's the hardest thing you can do. The devil is all around us." I reached down to assist him to his feet. "Here, Sir, let me help you up. We can go to the mission and drink cocoa and talk about Jesus . . . I know it's hard."

The man pushed my hand away. "What's so hard about bullying and bribing an old man?"

He staggered to his feet and started down the street in the direction opposite to the mission. He began to fall, we grabbed him and he passed out on us. Alfred and I put one of his arms around each of our shoulders and carried him to the mission.

I quit the Hi-C. I didn't exactly quit; it was the week before Easter and my dad told me he was having rush business and that he wanted me to help him every night until after the holidays. So I missed Hi-C meetings and the Youth-for-God rally and in order to get to work early I went to morning labs and I just never went back.

11

IF THE SUN, OR A STREETLIGHT hits a puddle of water at a certain angle it looks like a sheet of ice and I might stare at it for a lifetime, a few seconds, plunging reminder by reminder into the past.

There is something wonderful and sad about Ohio around Christmastime—maybe the reasons are the licentious, Yukon sleddog cold and the buildings on the main streets of college towns standing respectfully buttressed with graceful wings of dirty snow, or without snow, brazenly naked, watching the people plop by in galoshes. Maybe it is the students the last few days before vacation only making the motions of learning, already at home in their minds. Finally, one noon vacation comes and the students desert the campuses, eager for home, still thinking of home as the place they talked about all semester, the place that increased in perfection with each retelling; not the real home where their parents didn't know quite how to treat them: proud, a bit stiff, a bit jealous. They dash to the mythical homes that through repetition have become realities in their minds—back home where the girls are more free, the boys handsomer, the pace more rapid, everything better and faster.

Our college town was too small for a major railway system so to get to a main artery, depending upon the direction in which we lived, we migrated to either a larger town west of the college, or to a city south of us. I usually hitchhiked. I would cut through the campus, which ended at mainstreet; deserted the campus resembled nothing so much as a graveyard. When I reached mainstreet I would turn right. I would walk to the edge of town with my bag—down mainstreet: past the combination police station, courthouse and fire station, past the restaurant and one of the two movie theaters—somewhere along mainstreet between the courthouse and restaurant with the sun flashing and glaring off the melting snow and wet bricks I would begin to think about dying and immortality—I would change the bag to the other hand, go past the dumpy ten-cent store, where behind the counters the over-rouged town girls would pat and pump their frowsy hair trying to make themselves look better whenever a college boy came into the store, still believing in Cinderella, or H. Alger. I would walk on down the street, past the bank—still thinking about dying and immortality and forever, but I wasn't sad, just the opposite, I wanted to scream with aliveness—when I came to the corner and started across the street the wind would dive into my clothing and slap my face, after I got across I'd duck into the sheltered alcove of the haberdashery standing there looking at the stock displayed for Christmas until I felt warm again, then I would walk on to the edge of town and wait for a lift. Maybe Christmastime was wonderfully sad because we were all doing something, or leaving behind something—I am not sure —maybe it was because we were trying to fill each precious, never-returning moment, because we suspected, as we were always being told, that we were in the best time of our lives and that things would never be so fresh and exciting again—I guess that could make Christmastime wonderful and sad.

I would finally get to the old train station in the next town. I loved that station. Inside students would be milling around; girls with stuffed puppies, bareheaded boys, everyone yelling greetings across to one another and making dates—Have a good time . . . I want to get my brother's Christmas gift . . . I'll be up to your house New Year's Day . . . Meet me in the lobby Monday. The station came to personify the beginning of vacation for me; however, it was not the warm, secure feeling, inside with the students that I loved most; instead, it was the outside, the first glimpse I would get as I arrived. There would be the sturdy old building a sootdirty orange color with weathered green trim. As I got closer I would see the main door, which was sprung, tilting mildly downward and always, even in the coldest weather, the door stood slightly ajar. Where the door began to scrape the asphalt from three-quarters open to where it stopped a couple of inches short of closing a depression had been worn in a deepening semicircle. The semicircle was filled with a shallow puddle of stiff water, the water probably melted each day when the sun was hottest, but around three-thirty, or four, when

I would finally get to the station it was always frozen again into a thin sheet of ice.

Reminder upon reminder I float back into the whole thing. I see her again sitting across the aisle of the coach. I was never glad when she died, but I got a thrill of something momentous and depraved and Dorian Grayish.

The train would arrive in a rush of steam and flashing wheels just as if it had been driven out of an old impressionistic painting. We would crowd around the special student coach, brilliant strokes of color in our loud college clothing against the dull gray train. I might catch a glimpse of the other Negro who lived in the Chicago area climbing aboard.

At Christmastime most interracial friendships thinned out in puffs of embarrassment to be resumed again after the holidays, when the parties and get-togethers were over; but, regardless of this fact and even if Marjorie and I happened to use the same coach entrance, which we tried to avoid, and met face to face we would only nod perfunctorily to one another and then carefully, proudly, choose seats in opposite ends of the coach. At college we were haunted with the idea that we might bunch together and segregate ourselves and at a football game for instance two Negroes never sat together unless they were on a date, we would spread ourselves among the rest of the student body with mathematical accuracy. Somehow, though, in my third year Marjorie and I wound up sitting across from each other in the coach. Marjorie sat with another girl and I was alone. She smiled at me and I smiled back. We smiled at one another simultaneously, then she changed her seat and came and sat next to me. There we were sitting together—congregating as a racial group, segregating ourselves, this was surprising enough in itself, but if you also considered my general standing at the time and if you also considered Marjorie's personality and status it was even more surprising.

Socially at my college a Negro girl led a horrible existence. Most of the Negro boys were on scholarships for the ministry and even though the boys outnumbered the girls two-to-one, unless she was very beautiful a Negro girl went completely dateless year in and year out. Every now and then a Negro romance suddenly materialized and the white students would fuss and fritter and aren't-they-the-perfect-couple over them, but these romances always involved the beautiful colored girls and Marjorie was far from beautiful. White girls who found themselves out in the cold in the looks department joined sororities and let their prettier sisters wheedle dates for them, but Negroes were not allowed to join sororities and fraternities. The campus was geared to the fraternal societies and if you didn't belong there was a big sea of loneliness surrounding you. Oh, there was the thirty-man lifeboat of Negro companionship that we all clung to—the lifeboat was in very poor condition though, it leaked terribly; we were ashamed because the lifejackets of school pride we were issued didn't seem to hold us up very well, perhaps life had let the air out of our preservers, maybe Negroes weigh more, or something, anyway we were ashamed that the lifejackets weren't sufficient and even as we huddled together in the tossing, leaking vessel, each person clutching his tools and bailing furiously against the lonely water, we denied that the lifeboat existed. Negro boys bailed with sports and church and the girls bailed with dates when they could get them and with every campus activity opened to them, specializing in Samaritanlike organizations. The girls worked very diligently in their activities and they usually rose to high positions by the time they were upper classwomen. I think Marjorie was in more organizations than anyone in the school. Her picture appeared everywhere in the yearbooks. In my mind I always saw some girl going through the yearbook with her mother pointing to Marjorie's picture and saying, she lived in the dorm with me. . . . Oh, she was a swell person . . . so kind and sweet. Marjorie was kind and sweet, in fact, all the Negroes were—never getting angry, never saying bad things of other students, never borrowing clothing, never acting shitty, never cutting classes, or breaking training—we were perfect. Sometimes I would see Marjorie flitting across the campus from meeting to meeting, planning packages to be distributed to the local poor, or helping to organize a group to visit The Home for Wayward Girls. She would greet people with that whimsical, reassuring smile that she wore, that most of the Negro students wore—Oh, Yes, the smile said, We love it here (we're wonderfully adjusted). We were model students, from time to time someone would deviate and rock the boat, but in general we presented a one hundred percent front of integrity and goodwill.

I was one of the big deviators. Once a puzzled teacher summed up the general situation, he asked me, "Why can't you be like the rest of your er . . . er . . . people, they're adjusted? Do you know that you're the only Negro student that ever handed in a theme to me late? Did you know Charles Rollins? No, no, he left before you came. He was a wonderful lad, a Negro . . . just like yourself. Charles was a four letter man and president of his class twice!" then the teacher leaned back into his chair and put his feet upon his desk regular-guy fashion and beamed at me.

I never deviated to the extent that the boat was in danger of capsizing or anything like that, still, all in all, I wasn't too popular and I wondered why Marjorie who was very shy and whom I always thought of as the epitome of correctness had changed seats to sit with me. To change seats to sit with someone is an overt action, and as I said, at college Marjorie was very timid—of course, being out of the inner circle that Marjorie belonged to suddenly showing her soul to me, or doing something with me had the same embolding distance, yet longed for intimacy as talking to or doing something with a stranger met on a Greyhound, or in a public library. Now with the perspective, or rather, with the honesty of time, I believe she was desperately lonely, even with all the meetings, even going home for Christmas, she was suffocatingly lonely. If I suspected a little of her solitude at the time I refused it, I shut it out of my mind, I preferred to think that the cynical outcast-of-the-islands role that I was playing that semester had hopelessly ensnared her heart.

When you first met Marjorie, even before she spoke, you could tell she had made a truce with her looks. Her entire manner seemed to say—I'm going to talk to you like I'm just another girl, but I know I'm not so pretty, don't worry I won't be a bother. Marjorie was retiring and obsequious and everyone seemed to love her.

When she sat down, I cooled it and she had to open the conversation.

"How are you, Ed?"

"Bien," I said, letting it drop.

"Glad to be going home," she said (trying again).

I thought of Chicago just before Christmas when I

was little with the crowds bustling along in the Loop and my mother holding my hand—it would get dark, a slight snow might fall . . .

"I think it will be nice to get home," she said.

"Yeh, sure, yes . . . it will be."

A slight snow might fall and Christmas carols would float down from the cold impassive skyscrapers, like portly, dignified ladies singing in church. In the store windows there would be dwarfs, Santas, reindeer— even in my age-conscious college years I still thought of home around Christmastime just as it had been when I was a little boy, when with my mitten in my mother's hand I was tugged along in the wonderful loop crowds.

"I never see you around the upperclass dorms," she persisted. "Are you going with a freshman girl?"

"No, I don't have a girl (significant pause) . . . at the college." I had to turn my head away a little as we talked because her breath smelled. She was always spick-and-span, neat as a pin, cleanliness next to godliness, but her breath smelled a little.

We talked along.

"Where do you live in Chicago, on the south side?" she said.

"No, I live in the suburbs."

In the front of the coach some students had started to sing and their voices filled in the spaces betwen our words. Behind us a bridge game was going.

"Why don't you come around to the dorm and talk to me some time, Ed? Upperclass girls can stay out until eleven on weekdays and until one o'clock on Saturdays."

I turned and looked at Marjorie. In the slang of our college coming up to talk to someone meant taking them out. I never expected quiet little Marge to suggest that we start dating.

"Your friends wouldn't like that," I said.

(SILENCE)

"Look," I said, "You're nice . . . but something has got to be happening. (What I meant was she would have to sleep with me if I took her out.) I mean you have to put down something more than conversation." I sat under a palm tree with a filthy beard drinking wine, no one on the island liked me, except the chief's beautiful daughter who was asking to come and live with me.

"I know what you mean," she said. Marge understood me, and she agreed and I knew she'd never welch. Quiet, starchy, puritanical, obsequious Marge willing to trade herself, willing to trade what she probably considered her soul, for a little glitter and companionship— that was the first time I had an inkling of the depth of the human heart and what a dreamer it is and how lonely it could be.

I nodded agreement to the terms of the bargain.

We sat there a while, not saying anything. It was twilight and the landscape flashed past, a road, then a town, then farmland, then a road again. I remembered all the big deal activities on the campus, the dances, rallies, hayrides and assorted games: I was sure Marjorie had never been asked. Maybe at some time or other she went alone, or with a group of laughing, yapping, unhappy girls, but I was sure no fellow ever asked her. At home for her parents Marjorie probably had to pretend her college life was a mad social whirl. You know how parents are, they may be the first to admit their children's defects, but deep down they don't believe a word of it, or if they do see defects in their children, they build compensating virtues to balance things out. Parents don't see their children as ugly, or unattractive, even if they say they do. Also, Marge's parents probably hardly considered the fact that Marjorie was a Negro. That phenomenon, that much brighter tomorrow, was the direct result of the old hard-sell applied to the American Dream for a couple of centuries and until recently, no matter how bitter or disillusioned people were with their lot and/or the system, when their children were born they dragged out and polished up the old Up-the-Ladder-Dream. They were dead positive that life would be kinder to their children (anyway, the reality people face for themselves they often cannot bear to face for their children). Our parents begin to use rosy phrases that they once laughed at . . . GREAT PROGRESS, BETTER NOW, PEOPLE MORE INTELLIGENT, etc. In time, they completely subdued their fears and assumed that college, the future, our lives, everything, was for us just as the dream implied it was.

"Let's go out this coming Friday," I asked Marge, "the . . ." I took my wallet out and looked the date up on a pocket calendar. "The 23rd . . . O.K.?"

"Won't you be busy?" Marge said. I had caught her unprepared and she had relapsed into her old obsequious self. "Don't you have something else planned . . . I mean I don't want to upset . . ."

"Look," I interrupted, "if you've got some guy on the hook and you're all booked up . . . O.K., say so, but don't try to let me down easy."

She grinned with pleasure and it was a nice moment for us, sitting in the coach speeding into the deepening twilight. I wonder if she had lived if her life would have been nice moments, or a tunnel of affable loneliness.

Before I left the train we made a date for the 23rd.

When the big Friday came I borrowed my dad's car, wiped it off, put a blanket in the back seat and drove into Chicago to pick Marjorie up. Her parents buzzed around us, elated, evidently feeling that now their daughter had arrived and would begin to date steady.

I took her to some of the cheaper nightclubs that rudely shoulder one another for attention along 63rd Street; outside catchy neon signs, inside darkness and second rate plushness. It was the first time Marge had been nightclubbing and she enjoyed herself immensely. I liked her, against her naïveté I seemed blasé and sophisticated. We came out of a bar about twelve-thirty, it had been snowing but it had stopped except for an occasional big, lazy flake from the sky, or a torrent of gritty diamonds shaken loose from the tracks when a late "L" rattled past overhead. Suddenly it was time to seal the pact, we both knew it and we were embarrassed. I took her elbow until we got to the car. When I opened the door for her, one of us said something simple and we laughed. We drove through a nearby residential section looking for a dim place to park. The top and fenders of the cars along the streets each had a thin blanket of white. My dad didn't have a radio in the car but the tires hummed cosily on the slushy street. We found a place and parked, then, suddenly, it was quiet.

You know, to me, there is always something old-shoeish about making love. Perhaps the bed is different, or the motel, or the park, maybe the partner, or method is new; nevertheless, what, or how many things are new to me, when we put our arms around one another and sink down, after a moment, nothing seems unusual—there is a sudden sharp stream of familiarity and nothing, even if it is in an apartment doorway, or under a

143

tarpaulin on a crowded beach seems unusual. But first, before you sink down, there is the terrible period of small talk, when you babble back and forth to one another, neither paying any attention to what is said, just filling up the space everyone feels it is necessary to wait before they begin to make love. We sat in the front seat while talking and then we got into the back seat to seal the bargain.

"What are you majoring in, Marge?" I said. I had thrown the blanket over us. Under the blanket I began to unbutton her coat, then I put my hands on her waist. Her hands stopped mine automatically, then remembering herself she let me continue.

"European History," she said. I put my hand on her shoulders, she leaned back out of the streetlight—now completely in the noncommittal shadow of the seats—I started rubbing her breasts and she began to breathe deeper. She took one of my hands from under the blanket and kissed it and I was unhappy for a moment.

"What are you going to do when you graduate?" I asked.

"I don't know for sure yet . . . I don't know for sure," she said. I eased her into a comfortable position, then I put my hand on her leg, and started it up, along her stocking—I loved to do that when a girl had on stockings, run my hand up her leg, when I came to the top of her stocking and felt her soft flesh, the same good and honest flesh you hardly notice at the beach, it always gave me a thrill, it was different, at the top of a stocking it was wrong and nasty and wonderful.

"My dress is getting all mussed," she said.

"Pull it up neatly," I told her. I could feel her pulling her dress up. I unfastened the top of her dress and

144

pulled it and her slip down from her shoulders, then I took her breasts from her brassiere.

"Sit up," I said.

"Why Honey?"

"I want to look at you, sit up . . . just for a minute, so the streetlight falls on you." She sat up and I pulled the blanket completely away and looked at her. I looked at her, with her dress pulled up around her waist and down off her shoulders, with the brassiere cutting awkwardly under her exposed breasts and I felt like, I guess, a mountain climber feels at the summit. Shit—suddenly I owned the world—don't I have this broad right here of her own asking. Hell, man, I can operate. I eased her back into the shadows. "Take off your panties," I said. You do it, I thought, you do it, show me you want me. I'm not a big-headed sissy. She took off her pants. She was crying softly. I began to rub her and explore.

"What's the matter?" I said.

(Sniffling)

"This is the first time, isn't it?"

(Sniffling, softer)

I realized I didn't want to keep the bargain with Marjorie. Of course, I could have laid her and then welched on my part of the bargain, but, at the time bargain breakers, liars, welchers, promise forgetters and cheats in general composed the cornerstone of my hate against the world and I didn't want to compromise my scorn.

"If this is the first time then a car isn't the right place," I said, excusing myself. I talked on about positions and pain. She dressed and we kissed awhile. I noticed I could see my breath and we realized the car had become cold so I took her home. Later in bull sessions back at college, I bragged about that night, about not making her, not mentioning her name. "Cats," I would say, "it was the one decent thing I ever did."

I didn't see Marjorie anymore during Christmas vacation. A week after school reopened I happened to meet her in front of the student union.

"Hi, Marjorie," I said.

"Hi, Ed, are you ready for exams?" she said.

"I hope so," I said. We talked back and forth just scratching the surface of what we were wondering and what we wanted to know, feinting around for an opening into the other's attitude. Finally, Marge opened the subject. The first spring breeze pushed me in the face. I still didn't want to make the bargain with Marge.

"Are you going to come by sometime, Ed?" she said. She smiled at me—it had probably started out as a smile of encouragement or obsequious seduction, but through force of habit it ended up the NEGRO (we like it here) SPECIAL.

I told her, I would be glad to come by if I didn't think my roommate would kill me. She wanted to know why he would kill me and who was my roommate. Charles. She didn't know him. I told her that he knew her and he really liked her. She brightened, but she didn't know him. There aren't that many Negroes around, I said. You must have seen him. No. He drives an old black car. Now she remembered, but she hardly ever saw him. Anyway, I said, he knows you and he likes you. Well then why hadn't he ever said anything at all. I said he was only a sophomore and she was a senior. Well she didn't really think what class a person was in made any difference. Did I? No, I didn't think it made a bit of difference. Was I teasing? Hell, no. But why hadn't he ever said anything. You know how it

146

is, I said. I said I had to get to work and that I would see her later and I left.

That night when my roommate came in I called him over to my desk. "Say, Cat, do you know who digs you?"

"Who?"

"Marjorie that sorta cute little senior girl that . . ."

"Who?"

"Look, lover, this is only your old roomy . . . I mean you can tell me." He tried to explain and I hurried on. "Look you must know her. She's a quiet little girl (motions as if I am trying to explain myself better) my homey . . . from Chicago. She told me she liked you when we rode home Christmas—I know (puzzled motions) it seems funny," that's it, bring up any shaky part yourself. "I saw her again today and she mentioned you." My roommate put his hands in his pockets and rocked on his heels masculinelike. "Give her a call, Cat . . . call her up, Honeybunch."

"What for?" He sauntered over to his desk and picked up his pipe and tried to light it.

"You won't regret it, Motherdear," I said omnisciently.

(Aw what the hell)

"But how do you . . ."

I interrupted him, pretending to lose my temper which always adds credulity. "Look, Motherdear, I just told you . . . I mean, don't give me a hard time. Believe me it's a good deal, if you take it or not is up to you, you know what I mean?"

In our room which was on the west side of the dorm twilight lingered and lingered and when night would finally come it didn't seem like night at all, but only a darker twilight and the room always had a semi-mole

147

atmosphere, anyway my roommate stood in the false twilight with his feet apart and his pipe lit glaring at me. Maybe, I thought I poured it on too thick, but finally he said.

"What's her telephone number, Motherdear?" I gave it to him and he went and called her at her dorm.

After they started going together they would drive to Columbus every Sunday and spend the day. Once Marjorie managed to get a weekend off and they spent it together in a motel near Ohio State that would take Negroes.

"Cat," my roommate told me after he came back from his first date with her, "Thank You!"

"What happened, man?" I said.

He rolled his eyes.

I didn't see Marjorie for almost a month and a half after my roommate started going with her—when I did finally meet her she seemed like quite a different person. Marjorie was in love: she was in love with my roommate, she was in love with being somebody, she was in love with the sparkle she thought love had brought to her, she was in love with being with a group of girls and looking up at the clock and letting out a little gasp and flurrying out to get dressed for her date. When I met her she seemed, at least contrasted to her old manner, haughty and I was irritated with her. I secretly wished I had gotten into her pants when I had the chance and in the bullsessions when I told the story, "Cat, I knew this little chick, well anyway, we were in the back seat . . . it was all arranged, but she cried and I let her go," I was tempted to break my code and use her name, "It was the only good thing I ever did."

I only remember meeting her once, face to face, after that. We passed one another in front of the library. I expected her to be very haughty, but she seemed more like her old worried, apologetic self. She slowed down as if she had something to ask me, but I only nodded and passed her. Spring came to the campus; jerky, hopeful, uncertain like a fat girl trying to make friends—a false summer day here and there and winter would be completely forgotten and everyone would talk about flies and picnics, but the next day a light slushy snow would fall and we would joke about old man winter really hanging on: then rainy days and finally the trees would turn green and it would be spring. Sometimes I saw her flitting across the campus going to a meeting, or to my roommate.

A month after I passed her at the library I opened the college newspaper and discovered she had died, her obituary was on the second page:

> Last night the campus lost a stellar student. Marjorie (Marge) Kathryn Chambers, died in the Municipal Hospital of blood poisoning. Sunday she was admitted to the college infirmary after she had complained of a sore throat and headache to her roommate, Betty Sparks, and had been persuaded to go to the infirmary. When it was discovered she was suffering from blood poisoning she was rushed to the Municipal Hospital where she died at six-twenty last night. Marjorie had received the poisoning through a wound in her left foot that had been uncared for. Marjorie was . . .

it went on to tell how active she was in organization, how we would all miss her and how well liked she was.

I put the paper down.

I got up from my desk where I had been sitting and

went over to the window and looked out at the campus. I felt sorry—suddenly I imagined myself in a bathrobe with a scarf around my neck, in a room with a beamed ceiling and a fireplace with the logs glowing briskly, receiving the news of someone's death. A car winding through the campus road caught my eye and snapped me back. I thought of what her life would have been— nothing came, so I read "Thanotopsis," "Dover Beach," and "To an Athlete Dying Young" from a poetry textbook that I had for a course I was taking. I wrote a poem and dedicated it to Marjorie. I can only remember two words and a phrase from the poem. The two words were "Brief deciduous" and the phrase was "Dying in the spring time."

Several people asked me, "Did you hear about Marge?" Yeh, I heard.

Years later I met a Negro collegemate and we began to talk about college, slipping automatically into the old slang manner of speaking that we had used, calling each other Motherdear and Honeybunch. We had a regular Old Home Week discussing the places and people we knew, reviewing scene after scene and person after person. Eventually we came to Marjorie.

That was tough, Cat, about Marjorie, I said. Yeh. Stepping on a tack and getting lockjaw, I said, she would have graduated that semester. He looked at me to see if I was serious. Didn't I know the story. Of course I knew the story. Oh, no I didn't he said, how gullible could a fellow be—stepping on a nail and getting tetanus. She had to die of tetanus, you can't print news like that if it isn't true, Motherdear, I said. He admitted she died of tetanus. The authorities couldn't change that, he said. Not many people die of lockjaw nowadays. I agreed. Why did Marge? I don't know, she

150

was just careless, I said. Not hardly, Cat. What do you mean, I said. She was trying to give herself an abortion, he said.

I thought back to her funeral service. It was held in the College Chapel. Her parents wanted it there, in college, because they felt that there was where Marjorie had been so happy. The Dean of Women read the sermon. Her voice was firm and regretful, it soared through the crowded chapel carrying such phrases as: great loss, typifying goodness, excellent future. All the clubs Marjorie had ever belonged to came en masse, each fraternity and sorority sent an official representative and all the Negroes were there scattered methodically throughout the funeral crowd. After the service everyone filed past for the last look. Everyone seemed pleased. The people in front of me ooohed and ahhed and doesn't she look natural, and isn't she sweet, when it came my turn I leaned over and looked in—the first thing I saw was that goddamn smile.

12

I GRADUATED FROM COLLEGE on a Sunday.

I was glad it was on a Sunday. The way I spent my Sundays had always varied very little from week to week. Of course, through the years my schedule had changed, but the changes were all big, easy-to-remember steps not gradual, smooth transitions as the week days were. It is physically impossible, but I have always wanted to have a party with myselves at various ages, to see what we thought of each other and things. The closest I could come to my party was on Sundays. Sometimes I would look back and ask myself, I wonder what I was doing at this time ten years ago. I always looked back to the same day of the week I was on and if it was on a Tuesday, or say a Saturday I would usually have no idea what I had been doing, but on a

Sunday it was easy to do. When I was very little all I can remember about Sundays are the newsboys yelling and polished white shoes. Later as I grew older I remember I would go to church with Mother and sometimes Dad and I would listen very carefully to the sermon because at dinner my relatives would question my cousins and I about what the minister had said. In high school on Sundays I would dress real sharp and go to Sunday School and then come back home and fool around until it was showtime and then I would meet the rest of the gang and we'd go to the movies and when I got home Mother would tell me I was just on time, or scold me for being late and we'd have a big dinner with stewed chicken and rice, or a roast with brown gravy. In college Sunday morning I would go down to the Student Union where I ate meals and have brunch. Then afterward by myself, or with a buddy or two of mine who lived in the same dorm I did, I would walk back to my room, taking the roundabout way, walking through town instead of cutting across the campus. On the way back to the dorm students would go past heading for church. If it was raining they would have their heads down and wear tan raincoats. If it was a clear day the boys would saunter along in fraternal clusters wearing dark blue suits, or gray suits and the girls would wear gray suits, or blue suits, or flowered dresses with pink hats, shoes and purses.

As I walked over to pick up my parents from the colored lady's house where I had found a place for them to stay, I pretended I was having a party of me's. I was a piece of each Sunday of the Sundays I had lived through.

When I got there my parents were sitting in the lady's parlor ready to go. The lady asked me to put on

154

my gown so she could see how I looked and I put it on for a few minutes. We got up to go. When we reached the front door Mother remembered she didn't have a handkerchief and she asked Dad to go back into their bedroom and get one out of her suitcase. The lady had gone to the kitchen and Mom and I were alone for the first time since Friday afternoon when she and Dad had arrived. My Dad had heart trouble and Mom began to talk about his health.

Your father isn't well, Mom said. Sometimes he comes home from work so tired he's almost half out of his mind. He takes heart medicine, but I don't think it does him any good. He should take it easier . . . I try to tell him, we can get along I told him without him working himself to death. Mother paused and asked me didn't I have anything to say, wasn't I sorry. I said of course I was sorry Dad was sick. Mother said I didn't care and called me a heartless ungrateful. My Dad came back with a handkerchief and we left the house.

The weather was beautiful, the sky was light blue with low fluffy clouds and it was very sunny. My parents were dressed very nicely. My Dad had a new tan hat and when we got to the sidewalk he put it on. Dad had a regular ritual he went through to put a hat on.

First he would carefully inspect the crown and brim to be sure the hat was blocked exactly right, then he would hold the hat by the top upside in his right hand and jam it on his head in a graceful arcing motion, usually ruining the block he had just carefully inspected. Then he would run his hand along the brim to double check for dents, he would get out the dents, but more often than not the brim would end up twisted askew at a rakish angle the way gunmen were supposed to wear theirs in the '20's.

"Dad, your hat's crooked," I said.

My father looked at me apologetically. He took his hat off and straightened it and put it on very carefully, by the sides. It looked fine, but he double checked the brim twisting it to the rakish killer angle again.

"Here, Dad," I said and I reached up and straightened his hat. Then the three of us walked over to the campus.

On the way over Mother told me she had a new washing machine and she told me all about the poor trade-in she got on her old one. I asked her if she hadn't lost weight which always put her in a good mood. Mom giggled, then she caught herself. Humph, she said, you can't fool me . . . I'm fat and I know it . . . I'm proud of it too.

I walked my folks to the stadium and showed them the special entrance for the parents of the graduates, then I went back and found my place in the graduation procession. I slipped my robe on and got into line and after a little while, led by the faculty, we marched into the stadium. We had a prayer to open the commencement exercises and a few short speeches and then the main speaker talked.

I don't remember what he spoke about, I thought back to my high school graduation. The graduation was held at night, we sat in an ocean of collapsible chairs facing the rostrum. I can remember the speaker saying that when we're young we build castles in the air and when we grow up we settle for shacks by the roadside. The sun began to feel hot. I had on a loose fitting white shirt under my robe and I felt a drop of perspiration which must have fallen from my armpit hit my side and run down to my waistband. The speaker and officials stood on a platform that had been erected on the football field. The platform looked like a Nile barge, one like Cleopatra might have used, one like they always have miniatures of in the museums that people visit on rainy afternoons. I looked around at the faces of my classmates most of whom I would never see again. A cloud's shadow slowly passed along the football field. A light breeze sprang up. I looked around for my parents but I didn't see them. When the speaker finished talking awards were given out and then we filed along the stadium benches and down the steps and when our names were called we mounted the barge, walked up and received our diplomas. After the graduation was finished I met my parents and we walked over to my dorm which was adjacent to the stadium to get my bags.

It was about two or three in the afternoon. The sun was very bright, people poured along clustering around each graduate: parents, sharp aunts, thick ankled aunts, peasant uncles, sharp uncles, richer relations, poorer relations, envious relations, fiancees, close friends. Mother had me pose on the grass outside of my dorm in my robe and cap while she took some pictures. Then she decided she wanted to try and get some more commencement programs to take to her friends at home and she went back to the stadium.

I started to go around to pick up the car and bring it to the dorm. My dad called me.

"Let's wait here until your mother comes back," he said. We were still standing on the grass. Dad was holding his hat and his back was to the sun. I was facing the sun. I had taken off my cap and gown, but I put my cap back on to shield my eyes. People were going past on the sidewalk and graduates and their helpers were going in and out of the dorm loading cars, but we were in a little cove out of the stream of activity and the motion and noise didn't seem to reach us.

"I want to talk to you, Son," Dad said.

"Yes, Sir," I said.

My dad began to talk to me.

"Son," he said, "Mother and me, we are happy and proud of you, it is a great day for us. You did well in school. When you were a little boy I wanted to see you happy and safe at all costs. I had to earn a few dollars. There are things I want to talk about, things cross my mind. You are finishing college as time goes on you will always be working on something bigger and better. Remember, Son, life is a struggle—you've got to fight. Things will come your way in time just work hard and keep a clear mind. People are more in . . in . . intelligent than they used to be, but you must keep fighting. As a writer said in Biblical times, cast your eyes unto the hills."

I never grew to be as large as my dad and I had to look up to him a little as he talked.

"We must not hate, Big Guy," Dad said. "We must not hate, but love. We are children of a u . . universal family under the Fatherhood of God. I never pressed you to go to church, because being a Christian today usually means having your mind enslaved . . . I'm taking a course now, they send me pamphlets to help enlarge the mind and think about wondrous works of the Master. Your mother is a wonderful woman, but mothers will be mothers and they are the same the world around. She has always loved you as only a mother could. I know you think you are a man now, but you don't know anything about life. We have got to, as men, fight against many things and temptations. When I was your age I had been out in the world a long time. You have no idea, Son, no idea of what lies ahead. Always plan and look ahead. Myself, I've always been a dreamer. What is man without his dreams . . . map things out, plan. When I was starting out in the tailor shop, Stoker —you've heard me speak of him, had a good paying job, but where is he today? Nowhere he doesn't own a home, or anything. Why? Because he had no vision, no dream, no plan. One great writer said he would rather be a k . . king of the forest for a day than to be a lamb for a lifetime."

My mother came back and my dad put his left arm around her and they stood facing me. Mom began to cry.

"We love you, Son," Mother said. "I know you love your dad, but I don't think you love me."

"Yes, I do, Mother," I said.

"Do you, Son?" Mother said.

"Yes, I do, Mother," I said.

My dad squeezed Mom's shoulders and he began to blink his eyes. He put his hat on crushing the crown and he took out his handkerchief and gave it to my mother.

"You don't understand everything I have said, now, Son," my dad said, "but it will get clearer and clearer as you go along and begin to see life."

He stood with his arm around Mom and she had stopped crying and was trying to smile.

"Remember what I've tried to tell you, Son," he said.

"Yes, Sir," I said.

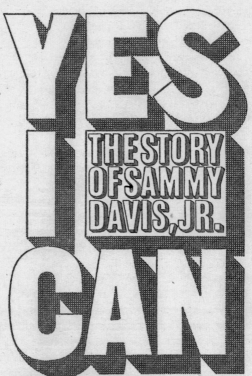

YES I CAN

THE STORY OF SAMMY DAVIS, JR.

BY SAMMY DAVIS, JR. AND JANE AND BURT BOYAR

95034/95¢

PUBLISHED BY
POCKET BOOKS
(G 1/9)